# ALBERT'S BRIDGE
# AND OTHER PLAYS

*Other Works by Tom Stoppard*
*Published by Grove Press*

Dirty Linen *and* New-Found-Land
Enter a Free Man
Jumpers
Lord Malquist and Mr. Moon
The Real Inspector Hound *and* After Magritte
Rosencrantz and Guildenstern Are Dead
Travesties

# TOM STOPPARD

# *ALBERT'S BRIDGE*
# *& Other Plays*

Grove Press, Inc.
New York

First Edition 1977
First Printing 1977
ISBN: 0-394-41339-3
Grove Press ISBN: 0-8021-0132-1
Library of Congress Catalog Card Number: 76-54489

First Evergreen Edition 1977
First Printing 1977
ISBN: 0-394-17000-8
Grove Press ISBN: 0-8021-4040-8
Library of Congress Catalog Card Number: 76-54489

Manufactured in the United States of America

Distributed by Random House, Inc., New York

GROVE PRESS, INC., 196 West Houston Street, New York, N.Y. 10014

# Contents

# ALBERT'S BRIDGE

*A play for radio*

*Albert's Bridge* received its first production on the BBC Third Programme on the 13th July 1967. The cast was as follows:

| | |
|---|---|
| BOB | Nigel Anthony |
| CHARLIE | Alexander John |
| DAD | Geoffrey Wincott |
| ALBERT | John Hurt |
| CHAIRMAN | Victor Lucas |
| DAVE | Ian Thompson |
| GEORGE | Anthony Jackson |
| FITCH | Ronald Herdman |
| MOTHER | Betty Hardy |
| FATHER | Alan Dudley |
| KATE | Barbara Mitchell |
| FRASER | Haydn Jones |

Produced by Charles Lefeaux

*Fade up bridge, with painting on mike. Four men are painting a big girdered railway bridge. They are spaced vertically, in ascending order:* BOB, CHARLIE, DAD, ALBERT. *To begin with, the mike is at* ALBERT'S *level, the top.*


BOB (*the most distant*): Char-lee!
CHARLIE (*less distant*): Hel-lo!
BOB: Right Charlie?
CHARLIE: Right! Comin' down! . . . Hey, Dad!
DAD (*an older man, not very distant*): Hel-lo!
CHARLIE: Bob 'n' me is done down here!
DAD: Right!
CHARLIE: Have you done?
DAD: Comin' down! . . . Albert! Al-bert!
CHARLIE (*more distant*): Albert!
BOB (*most distant*): Al-bert!
ALBERT (*very close, crooning softly, tunelessly amid various tunes while painting*):
    How high the moon in June?
    how blue the moon when it's high noon
    and the turtle doves above
    croon out of tune in love
    saying please above the trees
    which when there's thunder you don't run under
    —those trees—
    'cos there'll be pennies fall on Alabama
    and you'll drown in foggy London town
    the sun was shi-ning . . . on my Yiddisher Mama.
BOB (*most distant*): Albert!
CHARLIE (*less distant*): Albert!
DAD (*off*): Albert!
ALBERT: Hel-lo!

9

DAD: Bob 'n' me 'n' Charlie's done!

ALBERT: Right!

Dip-brush-slap-slide-slick, and once again, dip,
brush, slap—oh, it goes on so nicely . . . tickle it into the
corner, there, behind the rivet. . . . No one will see that
from the ground; I could cheat up here. But I'd know; so
dip, brush, slap, slide and once again for the last time till
the next time—every surface sleek, renewed—dip, brush,
slap, slick, tickle and wipe—right in there with the old
rust-proof rust-brown—all glossed and even, end to end—
the last touch—perfection! (*Painting stops.*) Oh my! I
could stand back to admire it and fall three hundred feet
into the sea. Mind your heads! (*Laughs. Climbing down.*)
Mind your head, Dad!

DAD: I'm not your dad. Keep off the wet—work down the
slope to the middle—and watch your feet.
(*Everyone climbing down, the distance between them closing.*)
Going down for good, oh yes, I'm not facing that again.
Ten coats I've done, end to end, and now I'm done all
right. I had ambitions, you know. . . .

CHARLIE (*nearer*): Mind my head, Dad.

DAD: Watch my feet, Charlie—comin' down——

CHARLIE: I'll watch your feet—you mind my head. Watch
your head, Bob——

BOB (*nearer*): Watch your feet, Charlie——

CHARLIE: Mind my feet Bob—watch my head, Dad. . . .

DAD: I'm not your dad, and mind my feet—that's my head,
Albert.

ALBERT: Comin' down. . . . Doesn't she look beautiful?

DAD: Looks the same as always. There's no progress. Twenty
years, twenty thousand pots of paint . . . yes, I had plans.

CHARLIE: I thought we'd never see the end of it.

BOB: It's not the bleeding end.

CHARLIE: There's no end to it.

DAD: Ten coats non-stop, one after the other, and it's no
improvement, no change even, just holding its own against
the weather—that's a long time, that's a lot of paint. I
could have made my mark.

ALBERT: Continuity—that's hard to come by.

DAD: I've spread my life over those girders, and in five minutes I could scrape down to the iron, I could scratch down to my prime.

ALBERT: Simplicity—so . . . contained; neat; your bargain with the world, your wages, your time, your energy, your property, everything you took out and everything you put in, the bargain that has carried you this far—all contained there in ten layers of paint, accounted for. Now that's something; to keep track of everything you put into the kitty, to have it lie there, under your eye, fixed and immediate—there are no consequences to a coat of paint. That's more than you can say for a factory man; his bits and pieces scatter, grow wheels, disintegrate, change colour, join up in new forms which he doesn't know anything about. In short, he doesn't know what he's done, to whom.

DAD: Watch your feet, Albert. Mind your head, Charlie.

CHARLIE: You mind my head. Take care my feet, Bob——

BOB: Watch your feet, Charlie——

CHARLIE: Mind your feet, Dad——

DAD: That's my head, Albert——

ALBERT: Coming down. . . .

Ah, look at it up there, criss-crossed and infinite, you can't see where it ends—I could take off and swing through its branches screaming like a gibbon!

DAD: Mind where you're putting your feet, Albert.

CHARLIE: Watch my head, Dad.

BOB: Train coming, Charlie.

(*Distant train coming.*)

CHARLIE: I've seen it.

BOB (*jumping down on to gravel*): And down.

CHARLIE: Mind where you jump, Dad.

DAD: Seen it.

CHARLIE (*jumping down*): None too soon.

DAD: Train coming, Albert.

ALBERT: I'm with you.

DAD (*jumps down*): Finished.

CHARLIE: Like hell.

BOB: Well, that's another two years behind you.

DAD: A feller once offered me a half share in a very nice trading station in the China Seas. I had it in me.

ALBERT: Mind your toes.

(*He jumps. Climbing down ends. All are now on mike.*)

Now that's a good way to end a day—ending so much else.

CHARLIE: All right for some. Students.

BOB: Slummers.

CHARLIE: Pocket-money holiday lads, oh yes.

ALBERT: One bridge—freshly painted—a million tons of iron thrown across the bay—rust brown and even to the last lick—spick and span, rust-proofed, weather-resistant—perfect!

DAD: Other end needs painting now. A man could go mad.

(*The train arrives and goes screaming past.*)

(*Set* CHAIRMAN *over end of train, cutting bridge.*)

CHAIRMAN: Let us not forget, gentlemen, that Clufton Bay Bridge is the fourth biggest single-span double-track shore-to-shore railway bridge in the world bar none——

DAVE: Hear, hear, Mr. Chairman——

CHAIRMAN: Thank you, Dave—

GEORGE: I've been studying these figures, Mr. Chairman——

CHAIRMAN: Just a moment, George. We've got an amenity here in Clufton, that bridge stands for the whole town, quite apart from the money earned in railway dues——

DAVE: Hear, hear, Mr. Chairman——

CHAIRMAN: Thank you, Dave.

GEORGE: According to the City Engineer's figures, Mr. Chairman——

CHAIRMAN: Just a moment, George. When my grandfather built this bridge he didn't spare the brass—and I for one, as chairman of the Clufton Bay Bridge Sub-Committee— entrusted as we are with the upkeep and responsibility of what is a symbol of Clufton's prosperity—I for one do not begrudge the spending of a few extra quid on a lick of paint.

DAVE: Hear, hear, Mr. Chairman.

CHAIRMAN: Thank you, Dave.

GEORGE: I know it's a symbol of your prosperity, Mr. Chairman, but——

CHAIRMAN: That's a highly improper remark, George. Clufton's prosperity is what I said.

DAVE: Hear, hear, Mr. Chairman.

CHAIRMAN: Thank you, Dave.

GEORGE: My mistake, Mr. Chairman—but if Mr. Fitch's figures are correct——

FITCH (*distinctive voice; clipped, confident; rimless spectacles*): My figures are always correct, Mr. Chairman.

CHAIRMAN: Hear that, George? The City Engineer's figures are a model of correctitude.

DAVE: Hear, hear, Mr. Chairman.

CHAIRMAN: Thank you, Dave.

GEORGE: Then this new paint he's recommending is going to cost us four times as much as the paint we've been using up to now.

(*Pause.*)

CHAIRMAN: Four times as much? Money?

DAVE: Hear, hear, Mr. Chairman.

CHAIRMAN: Just a moment, Dave. I don't think your figures are correct, George. Mr. Fitch knows his business.

GEORGE: What business is he in—paint?

CHAIRMAN: That's a highly improper remark, George—er, you're not in the paint business, are you, Mr. Fitch?

FITCH: No, Mr. Chairman.

CHAIRMAN: No, no, of course you're not. You should be ashamed, George.

DAVE: Hear, hear, Mr. Chairman.

CHAIRMAN: Shut up, Dave. Now what about it, Mr. Fitch—is this right what George says?

FITCH: Well, up to a point, Mr. Chairman, yes. But in the long run, no.

CHAIRMAN: Don't fiddle-faddle with me, Fitch. Does this new-fangled paint of yours cost four times as much as the paint we've got, and if so, what's in it for you?

GEORGE: Hear, hear, Mr. Chairman.

CHAIRMAN: Thank you, George.

FITCH: To put the matter at its simplest, Mr. Chairman, the new paint costs four times as much and lasts four times as long.

CHAIRMAN: Well, there's your answer, George. It costs four times as much but it lasts four times as long. Very neat, Fitch—I thought we'd got you there.

GEORGE: What's the point, then?

FITCH: Apart from its silvery colour, Mr. Chairman, which would be a pleasanter effect than the present rusty brown, the new paint would also afford a considerable saving, as you can no doubt see.

CHAIRMAN: Everybody see that? Well, I don't.

GEORGE: Nor do I.

DAVE: Hear, hear, George.

GEORGE: Shut up, Dave.

FITCH: If I might explain, gentlemen. As you know, in common with other great bridges of its kind, the painting of Clufton Bay Bridge is a continuous operation. That is to say, by the time the painters have reached the far end, the end they started at needs painting again.

DAVE: I never knew that!

CHAIRMAN AND GEORGE: Shut up, Dave.

FITCH: This cycle is not a fortuitous one. It is contrived by relating the area of the surfaces to be painted—call it A— to the rate of the painting—B—and the durability of the paint—C. The resultant equation determines the variable factor X—i.e. the number of painters required to paint surfaces A at speed B within time C. For example——

CHAIRMAN: E.g.

FITCH: Quite. Er, e.g. with X plus one painters the work would proceed at a higher rate—i.e. B, plus, e.g. Q. However, the factors A and C, the surface area and the lasting quality of the paint remain, of course, constant. The result would be that the painters would be ready to begin painting the bridge for the second time strictly speaking before it needed re-painting. This creates the co-efficient—Waste.

CHAIRMAN: W.

FITCH: If you like. This co-efficient belies efficiency, you see.

CHAIRMAN: U.C. You see, George?

GEORGE: OK, I see.

FITCH: To continue. Furthermore, the value of the co-efficient—Waste—is progressive. Let me put it like this, gentlemen. Because the rate of painting is constant, i.e. too fast to allow the paintwork to deteriorate, each bit the men come to requires re-painting even less than the bit before it. You see, they are all the time catching up on themselves progressively, until there'll come a point where they'll be re-painting the bridge, while it's still wet! (*Pause.*) No that can't be right. . . .

CHAIRMAN: Come to the point Fitch. Wake up, Dave.

DAVE (*waking up*): Hear, hear, Mr. Chairman.

FITCH: To put it another way, gentlemen, that is to say, conversely. With one too few painters—X minus one—the rate of progress goes down to let us say, B minus Q. So what is the result? By the time the painters are ready to start re-painting, the end they started at has deteriorated into unsightly and damaging rust—a co-efficient representing the converse inefficiency.

CHAIRMAN: Pull yourself together, Fitch—I don't know what you're drivellin' about.

GEORGE: In a nutshell, Fitch—the new paint costs four times as much and lasts four times as long. Where's the money saved?

FITCH: We sack three painters.

(*Pause.*)

CHAIRMAN: Ah. . . .

FITCH: You see, to date we have achieved your optimum efficiency by employing four men. It takes them two years to paint the bridge, which is the length of time the paint lasts. This new paint will last eight years, so we only need one painter to paint the bridge by himself. After eight years, the end he started at will be just ready for re-painting. The saving to the ratepayers would be £3,529 15s. 9d. per annum.

GEORGE: Excuse me, Mr. Chairman——

CHAIRMAN: Just a moment, George. I congratulate you, Mr. Fitch. An inspired stroke. We'll put it up to the meeting of the full council.

GEORGE: Excuse me——

CHAIRMAN: Shut up, George.

DAVE: Hear, hear, Mr. Chairman.

FITCH: Thank you, Mr. Chairman.

CHAIRMAN: Thank you, Mr. Fitch.

(*Fade.*)

MOTHER: Aren't you getting up, Albert? It's gone eleven. . . . Are you listening to me, Albert?

ALBERT (*in bed*): What?

MOTHER: I'm talking to you, Albert.

ALBERT: Yes?

MOTHER: Yes-what?

ALBERT: Yes, Mother.

MOTHER: That's better. Oh dear, what was I saying?

ALBERT: I don't know, Mother.

MOTHER (*sighs*): I was against that university from the start.

ALBERT: The country needs universities.

MOTHER: I mean it's changed you, Albert. You're thinking all the time. It's not like you, Albert.

ALBERT: Thinking?

MOTHER: You don't talk to me. Or your father. Well, I'm glad it's all behind you, I hope it starts to wear off.

ALBERT: I wanted to stay on after my degree, but they wouldn't have me.

MOTHER: I don't know what you want to know about philosophy for. Your father didn't have to study philosophy, and look where he is, Chairman of Metal Alloys and Allied Metals. It's not as if you were going to be a philosopher or some- thing. . . . Yes, you could have been a trainee executive by now. As it is you'll have to do your stint on the factory floor, philosophy or no philosophy. That university has held you back.

ALBERT: I'll have to get myself articled to a philosopher. . . .

Start at the bottom. Of course, a philosopher's clerk wouldn't get the really interesting work straight off, I know that. It'll be a matter of filing the generalizations, tidying up the paradoxes, laying out the premises before the boss gets in—that kind of thing; but after I've learned the ropes I might get a half share in a dialectic, perhaps, and work up towards a treatise. . . . Yes, I could have my own thriving little philosopher's office in a few years.

(*Pause.*)

MOTHER: Would you like to have some coffee downstairs?

ALBERT: Yes.

MOTHER: Yes-what?

ALBERT: Yes please.

(*Pause.*)

MOTHER: I still think it was mean of you not to let us know you had a summer vacation.

ALBERT: I thought you knew. I've had one every year.

MOTHER: You know I've no head for dates. You could have come home to see us.

ALBERT: I'm sorry—there was this temporary job going. . . .

MOTHER: Your father would have given you some money if you'd asked him.

ALBERT: I thought I'd have a go myself.

MOTHER: You'll have to get up now.

ALBERT: It was fantastic up there. The scale of it. From the ground it looks just like a cat's cradle, from a distance you can take it all in, and then up there in the middle of it the thinnest threads are as thick as your body and you could play tennis on the main girders.

MOTHER: Kate will be up in a minute to make the beds.

ALBERT: It's absurd, really, being up there, looking down on the university lying under you like a couple of bricks, full of dots studying philosophy——

MOTHER: I don't want you getting in Kate's way—she's got to clean.

ALBERT: What could they possibly know? I saw more up there in three weeks than those dots did in three years. I saw the context. It reduced philosophy and everything else. I got a

perspective. Because that bridge was—separate—complete—
removed, defined by principles of engineering which makes
it stop at a certain point, which compels a certain shape,
certain joints—the whole thing utterly fixed by the rules
that make it stay up. It's complete, and a man can give his
life to its maintenance, a very fine bargain.

MOTHER: Do you love me, Albert?

ALBERT: Yes.

MOTHER: Yes-what?

ALBERT: Yes please.

(*Cut to a gavel banged on table.*)

MAYORAL VOICE: Number 43 on the order paper, proposal from
Bridge sub-committee. . . .

VOICE 1: Move. . . .

VOICE 2: Second.

MAYORAL VOICE: All in favour.
(*Absent-minded murmur of fifty 'Ayes'.*)
Against. (*Pause.*) Carried. Number 44 on the order paper.
(*Fade.*)

(*Fade up knock on door off. Door opens.*)

KATE: Oh, I'm sorry, Mr. Albert.

ALBERT: Hello, I was just thinking of getting up.

(*Cut to.*)

BOB: What—by myself? It would take years.

FITCH: Eight years, yes.

BOB: No. I demand a transfer.

FITCH: I thought I'd give you first refusal.

BOB: I want to go back to painting the Corporation crest on the
dustcarts.

FITCH: I could fit you in on the magenta.

BOB: On the what?

FITCH: It's one man to a colour nowadays. Efficiency.
(*Cut.*)

CHARLIE: You must be joking.

FITCH: It's an opportunity for you.

CHARLIE: I'd go mad. What's it all about?

FITCH: Efficiency.

CHARLIE: I'm not doing that bridge on me tod.

FITCH: It's no more work than before.

CHARLIE: I'd jump off within a month.

FITCH: Oh. Well, we couldn't have that. That would be only one ninety-sixth of it done.

(*Cut.*)

DAD: You mean it's a cheaper way of doing it.

FITCH: More efficient.

DAD: We've been doing a good job.

FITCH: Efficiency isn't a matter of good and bad, entirely. It's a matter of the optimum use of resources—time, money, manpower.

DAD: You mean it's cheaper. I'm an old man.

FITCH: You've got eight years in you.

DAD: It might be my last eight. I haven't done anything yet— I've got a future.

FITCH: Well, I could put you on yellow no-parking lines.

DAD: Yes, all right.

(*Cut.*)

FITCH: . . . But do you have any qualifications?

ALBERT: I've got a degree in philosophy, Mr. Fitch.

FITCH: That's a little unusual.

ALBERT: I wouldn't say that. There were lots of us doing it.

FITCH: That's all very well if you're going to be a philosopher, but what we're talking about is painting bridges.

ALBERT: Yes, yes, I can see what you're driving at, of course, but I don't suppose it did me any harm. Almost everyone who didn't know what to do, did philosophy. Well, that's logical.

FITCH: You're an educated man.

ALBERT: Thank you.

FITCH: What I mean is, you're not the run-of-the-mill bridge painter, not the raw material I'm looking for.

ALBERT: Well, I did it in the vacation.

FITCH: Yes . . . yes, I did have reports of you. But surely. . . .

ALBERT: I know what you mean, but that's what I want to do. I liked it. I don't want to work in a factory or an office.

FITCH: Is it the open air life that attracts you?

ALBERT: No. It's the work, the whole thing—crawling round that great basket, so high up, being responsible for so much that is so visible. Actually I don't know if that's why I like it. I like it because I was happy up there, doing something simple but so grand, without end. It doesn't get away from you.

FITCH: The intellectual rather than the practical—that's it, is it?

ALBERT: Probably.

FITCH: I'm the same. It's poetry to me—a perfect equation of space, time and energy——

ALBERT: Yes——

FITCH: It's not just slapping paint on a girder——

ALBERT: No——

FITCH: It's continuity—control—mathematics.

ALBERT: Poetry.

FITCH: Yes, I should have known it was a job for a university man. . . .

ALBERT: Like me and you——

FITCH: Well, I went to night school myself.

ALBERT: Same thing, different time.

FITCH: That's what I say.

ALBERT: I'm your man, Mr. Fitch.

FITCH: You'll stick to it for eight years, will you?

ALBERT: Oh, I'll paint it more than once.

(*Cut.*)


(*Breakfast in background.*)

FATHER: Now then, Albert, you've had your fun. When I was your age I'd got six years of work behind me.

ALBERT: Well, I'm starting work now, father.

FATHER: Quite so, but don't think you're going to start at the top. You'll get there all right in time but you've got to learn the business first. Is there any more tea, Mother?

MOTHER: Ring for Kate, would you, Albert?

ALBERT (*going*): Yes, mother.

MOTHER: That reminds me.

FATHER: You'll start where I started. On the shop floor.

ALBERT (*approach*): Well, actually, Father——

MOTHER: I don't want to sound Victorian, but one can't just turn a blind eye.

ALBERT: What?

FATHER: Yes, I never went in for books and philosophy and look at me now.

MOTHER: I suppose that's the penance one pays for having servants nowadays.

ALBERT: What?

FATHER: I started Metal Alloys and Allied Metals—built it up from a biscuit-tin furnace in the back garden, small smelting jobs for the cycle-repair shop.

MOTHER: I've suspected her for some time and now one can't ignore it. Even with her corset.

ALBERT: Who?

FATHER: You can come in on Monday and I'll hand you over to the plant foreman.

ALBERT: I've already got a job. Actually.

FATHER: You haven't got a job till I give you one.

ALBERT: I'm going to paint Clufton Bay Bridge, starting Monday.

MOTHER: What colour?

ALBERT: Silver.

FATHER: Just a minute——

KATE (*off*): You rang, madam?

MOTHER: More tea, Kate, please.

KATE: Yes, madam.

MOTHER: And a word.

KATE: Yes, madam.

MOTHER: Are you ill?

KATE: No, madam.

MOTHER: I believe I heard you being ill in the bathroom, this morning.

KATE: Yes, madam.

MOTHER: And yesterday?

KATE: Yes, madam.

ALBERT: What's the matter, Kate?

KATE: Nothing, Mr. Albert.

MOTHER: Leave this to me. Cook tells me you fainted in the kitchen last week.

KATE: I came over funny.

ALBERT: Kate. . . .

MOTHER: Let's not beat about the bush. Is it the gardener's boy?

KATE: No, madam.

MOTHER: Then who is it?

ALBERT: Who's what?

MOTHER: Well, I'm sorry. You can have a month's wages, of course. You'd better make sure that the young man does the right thing by you.

(*Cut.*)

KATE: I never thought you'd do the right thing by me, Albert.

ALBERT: We'll be all right. It's a nice room.

KATE: Your mum didn't like it.

ALBERT: My mother's got no taste. I'll make a fire.

KATE: And wrap up warm when you go out—it'll be freezing up there.

ALBERT: Only a breeze.

KATE: It'll be ice in a month. If you fell I'd die, Albert.

ALBERT: So would I.

KATE: Don't you ever fall. They shouldn't make it a year-round job. It's dangerous.

ALBERT: No—you don't know how big it is—the threads are like ladders and the cross-pieces are like piers into the sky.

KATE: You hold on tight, for the spring, and the baby.

(*Cut in bridge and painting.*)

ALBERT: Slip, slap, brush, dip, slop, slide, slick and wipe. . . .
In eight years I'll be pushing thirty, and the Clufton Bay Bridge will be a silver bridge—dip-brush, slick, slide, slap without end, I'm the bridge man,

web-spinning silvering spiderman
crawling between heaven and earth on a
cantilevered span,
cat's cradled in the sky . . .
look down at the toy ships
where the sea pounds under toy trains to
toy towns
under my hand.
Am I the spider or the fly?
I'm the bridge man. . . .

The downstairs maid went upstairs to make a bed that I
was in—and suddenly——
(*Cut out bridge. Cut in crying baby.*)

I name this child Albert.
KATE: You can't.
ALBERT: Very well. I name this child Kate.
KATE: Katherine.
ALBERT: Tomorrow wheel her along to the bridge so I can see
you.
KATE: All right. But don't wave, Albert. Don't wave. If you
waved and fell——
ALBERT: I shan't wave.

(*Cut in bridge and painting.*)
Dip brush, dip brush
without end, come rain or shine;
A fine way to spend my time.
My life is set out for me,
the future traced in brown,
my past measured in silver;
how absurd, how sublime
(don't look down)
to climb and clamber in a giant frame;
dip brush, dip brush, slick, slide wipe
and again.
(*Painting stops.*)
I straddle a sort of overflowing gutter on which bathtub

boats push up and down. . . . The banks are littered with
various bricks, kiddiblocks with windows; dinky toys move
through the gaps, dodged by moving dots that have no
colour; under my feet the Triang train thunders across the
Meccano, and the minibrick estates straggle up over the
hill in neat rows with paintbox gardens. It's the most
expensive toytown in the store—the detail is remarkable.
But fragile. I tremble for it, half expecting some petulant
pampered child to step over the hill and kick the whole
thing to bits with her Startrite sandals.
(*Painting.*)
Don't look down,
the dots are looking up.
Don't wave, don't fall, tumbling down a
telescope, diminishing to a dot.
In eight years who will I be?
Not me.
I'll be assimilated then,
the honest working man, father of three—
you've seen him around,
content in his obscurity, come to terms with public truths,
digging the garden of a council house
in what is now my Sunday suit.
I'm okay for fifty years, with any luck;
I can see me climb
up a silver bridge to paint it for the seventh time,
keeping track of my life spent in painting in the colour of
    my track:
above it all.
How sublime
(dip brush, dip brush) silvering the brown.
Which dot is mine?
Don't wave, don't look down.
Don't fall.
(*Cut bridge.*)

KATE: I saw you today.
ALBERT: What was I doing?

KATE: Painting, I suppose. Crawling backwards along a cross-piece.

ALBERT: Pulling silver after me. I didn't see you. Or I didn't see which one was you.

KATE: Coming out of the hairdressers. Six and six, I had it cut.

ALBERT: Just goes to show—if you get far enough away, six and sixpence doesn't show, and nor does anything, at a distance.

KATE: Well, life is all close up, isn't it?

ALBERT: Yes, it hits you, when you come back down. How close it all is. You can't stand back to look at it.

KATE: Do you like my hair like this?

ALBERT: Like what? Oh—yes. Do you like mine?

KATE: I got whistled at in the street.

ALBERT: It's always happening to me.

KATE: A lorry driver, at the traffic lights.

ALBERT: They're the worst, I find.

KATE: Oh, Albert. I had the pram with me too.

ALBERT: You look too young for it. Big sister.

KATE: And I cook very nice, don't I?

ALBERT: I'd whistle at you.

KATE: I'd come, if you whistled. I'd give you a wink and say, 'Cheeky!'

ALBERT: Oh, yes—you'd get off with me. No trouble at all. I'd take you down by the canal after the pictures.

KATE: What do you know about it—with your education and all?

ALBERT: Me? I'm a working man.

KATE: You don't have regrets, do you, Albert?

ALBERT: No.

KATE: It wasn't a good bargain, on the face of it.

ALBERT: It depends on what you want.

KATE: Me and the baby. Two rooms and a forty-five hour week, hard work and no advancement.

ALBERT: I'm not ambitious.

KATE: You could have had so much—a white wedding, nice house, an office job with real prospects, the country club ... tennis. .... Yes, you could have had Metal Alloys and Allied Metals—the top job, responsibility, your own office with telephones. . . .

ALBERT: Yes, I'm well out of that.

(*Cut in bridge and painting.*)
Progress. Two lines of silver meeting in an angle bracket—
—and tickle in there behind the rivet—slip slop and wipe
and on we go up the slope.
Does the town look up? Do they all gawp and say to each
other, look at him! How ridiculous he looks up there, so
small, how laughably inadequate. Or do they say, How
brave! One man against the elements! Pitted against so
much!
The lone explorer feeling his way between the iron
crevasses, tacked against the sky by his boots and fingers.
Dots, bricks and beetles.
I could drown them in my spit.

(*Cut bridge, cut in baby's rattle in background.*)

KATE: That isn't nice, Albert.

ALBERT: Spitting?

KATE: Talking like that.

ALBERT: It doesn't represent desire. I'll let them live. I'm only
trying to tell you what it's like.

KATE: I know what it's like. It's painting a girder. There's other
jobs.

ALBERT: It's my bridge—I wish you'd stop her rattling, it's
getting on my nerves.

KATE: That's very advanced for six months.

ALBERT: I'm not doubting her progress. If she played the
trumpet it would be even more advanced but it would still
be sending me round the twist. Here, give——
(*He dispossesses the rattler, who bawls.*)

KATE: Now you've set her off. She doesn't *understand*.
(*Comforting.*) Come on, then. . . .

ALBERT: Well, see you later.

KATE: Where are you going?

ALBERT: Work.

KATE: It's your Saturday off.

ALBERT: No, it's my Saturday on.
KATE: Last Saturday was your Saturday on.
ALBERT: Well, I'll take two off in a row.

(*Cut in bridge.*)
Listen . . .
The hot sun makes you think of insects,
but this insect hum is the whole city
caught in a seashell. . . .
All conversation is hidden there,
among motors, coughing fits, applause,
screams, laughter, feet on the stairs,
secretaries typing to dictation,
radios delivering the cricket scores,
tapes running, wheels turning, mills grinding,
chips frying, lavatories flushing, lovers sighing,
the mayor blowing his nose.
All audible life in the vibration
of a hairdryer in the room below.
(*Painting.*)
Dip brush, slide, stroke,
it goes on as smooth and shiny
as my sweat. I itch.
Paint on my arm,
silver paint on my brown arm;
it could be part of the bridge.
(*Painting stops.*)
Listen. The note of Clufton is B flat.
The whole world could be the same.
Look down. Is it a fact
that all the dots have names?
(*Cut bridge.*)

KATE: Jack Morris is taking Maureen and little Leslie to Paris.
ALBERT: Who's Jack Morris?
KATE: Next door, Albert.
ALBERT: Oh yes. Who's Maureen?
KATE: Mrs. Morris.

ALBERT: So little Leslie would be their little girl.

KATE: It's a little boy.

ALBERT: Ah. Why are we talking about them?

KATE: They're going to Paris for a holiday. Where are we going?

ALBERT: When?

KATE: That's what I'd like to know.

ALBERT: What?

KATE: Don't you have a holiday?

ALBERT: Oh. I suppose I must. Everybody does. Yes, I expect Fitch took that into account.

KATE: You're not going to dodge your holiday—I know what you're up to, you're already working full Saturdays, don't think I'm such a fool that I don't know. . . . And you're working till dark.

ALBERT: Overtime. I lose time in the winter.

KATE (*sniffing*): It's because you don't like it here, being at home.

ALBERT: Oh, Kate . . . I've got a schedule, you see.

KATE: You're miles ahead of it.

ALBERT: I've got to have some in hand in case of accidents.

KATE: I told you! You'll fall off, and me and Katherine will be alone.

ALBERT: No, no, no . . . stop crying. We'll have a holiday. I'll take a week.

KATE: A fortnight.

ALBERT: All right, I don't mind.

KATE: Can we go to Paris?

ALBERT: I've been to Paris. There's nothing there, believe me. We could go to Scotland.

KATE: Touring?

ALBERT: Certainly. The Firth of Forth.

KATE: We haven't got a car. Maureen said we could go with them.

ALBERT: But they're going to Paris.

KATE: We could afford it. It wouldn't be hard, it's easier with two children and joined forces. . . . It would be lovely, I've always wanted to see the Champs Elysee and the Ark de Triumph and the Seine and the Eiffel Tower. . . .

(*Cliché French accordion music. Cross-fade to Eiffel Tower. It's the same as Clufton Bridge.*)
(*Distant. Shouting up.*) Albert! A-a-albert! (*Repeated, fading, despairing.*) Come down! Please come down!

ALBERT: I thought as much. Dots, bricks, beetles . . . in B flat. Still, I'm glad I came. The pointlessness takes one's breath away—a tower connects nothing, it stands only so that one can go up and look down. Bridge-builders have none of this audacity, compromise themselves with function. Monsieur Eiffel, poet and philosopher, every eight years I'll scratch your name in the silver of Clufton Bay Bridge.

KATE (*distant, despairing*): Al-bert!
ALBERT (*quiet*): Coming down.

(*Cut Eiffel Tower.*)
(*Crockery smashes, flung against wall.*)
KATE: What's her name?
ALBERT: Kate. . . .
KATE: What a bloody coincidence!
ALBERT: You've got it all wrong, Kate, there's no woman——
KATE (*crying*): I can smell her on your coat!
ALBERT: It's paint—I tell you I was up on the bridge.
KATE: All night!
ALBERT: I just thought I would. It was nice up there.
KATE: You're barmy if you expect me to believe that, you're round the twist——
ALBERT: It's true——
KATE: And I believe it, I *am* round the twist! I'm as barmy as you are, but I believe it——
ALBERT: That's better——
(*Another cup smashes.*)
KATE: No it isn't—it's worse! A woman would be normal. (*Breaking down.*) You don't talk to me, you don't talk to Katherine, you can't wait to get out of the house and up your favourite girder. (*Quieter, sobbing.*) You don't like me any more, I know you don't—I'm boring for you, I haven't got what you want, and you don't want to hear the things

I tell you because I've got nothing to tell you, nothing
happens. . . .

ALBERT: I like a quiet life, that's all.

KATE: Gutless. You'll spend your whole life painting that
bridge. . . .

ALBERT: It's a good job.

KATE: You know damn well it's a stupid job which any thick
idiot could do—but you're educated, Albert. You had
opportunities. There was Metal Alloys and Allied Metals—
you could have gone right up the ladder—we'd have a
house, and friends, and we'd entertain and Katherine
would have nice friends—you could have been an
executive!

ALBERT: I was lying in bed one day when the maid came in to
make it. . . . She was all starchy. When she moved, her
skirt sort of crackled against her nylons. . . . I never had
any regrets, but I did want her to be happy too.

KATE (*sobbing*): I've begun talking to myself, over the sink and
stove. . . . I talk to myself because nobody else listens, and
you won't talk to me, so I talk to the sink and the stove
and the baby, and maybe one day one of them will answer
me.

(*Baby gurgles, almost a word.*)

(*Cut to bridge and painting.*)

ALBERT (*crooning flatly amid and around the tune of 'Night and
Day'*):
Night and day, I am the one . . .
day and night, I'm really a part of me. . . .
I've got me under my skin.
So why
don't I take all of me
When I begin the beguine. . . .
I get accustomed to my face,
The thought of me makes me stop
before I begin
Yes, I've got me under my skin,
and I get a kick out of me. . . .

Day and night, night and day. . . .
Shall I compare me to a summer's day,
'Cos I can't get me out of my mind
I saw me in Monterey . . .
and I'm all right by me,
yes I'm all right, I'm all right,
I'm all right by me. . . .
(*Applause, two-handed, from quite close. Painting stops.*)
Who's there? Who's that?

FRASER (*applauding*): Very nice, very nice. The egotist school of
songwriting.

ALBERT: Who are you?

FRASER: You mean my name?

ALBERT: I suppose so.

FRASER: Fraser.

ALBERT: What are you doing on my bridge?

FRASER: Yours?

ALBERT: I'm painting it. I'm authorized.

FRASER: You've got a big job ahead of you.

ALBERT: I've got the time.

FRASER: You've got the time perhaps, but I'd say that time is
against you. The condition of the paintwork is very
shoddy.

ALBERT: Well, it hasn't been done for a fair while.

FRASER: Yes, it's beginning to look definitely tatty.

ALBERT: I'm getting through it bit by bit.

FRASER: Too slow. The old paint isn't lasting. People have
noticed, you know. There's been talk.

ALBERT: Look here—are you the bridge inspector or something.

FRASER: What?

ALBERT: Did Mr. Fitch send you?

FRASER: Who?

ALBERT: What's it all about then?

FRASER: Look down there. I came up because up was the only
direction left. The rest has been filled up and is still filling.
The city is a hold in which blind prisoners are packed wall
to wall. Motor-cars nose each other down every street, and
they are beginning to breed, spread, they press the people

to the walls by their knees, pinning them by their knees, and there's no end to it, because if you stopped making them, thousands of people would be thrown out of work, and they'd have no money to spend, the shopkeepers would get caught up in it, and the farms and factories, and all the people dependent on them, with their children and all. There's too much of everything, but the space for it is constant. So the shell of human existence is filling out, expanding, and it's going to go bang.

ALBERT: You're frightened of traffic?

FRASER: We are at the mercy of a vast complex of moving parts, any of which might fail. Civilization is in decline, and the white rhino is being wiped out for the racket in bogus aphrodisiacs.

ALBERT: An animal lover——

FRASER: That was merely a trifle I snatched at in my inability to express the whole. I have never been able to understand, for instance, why anyone should want to be a dentist. I cannot pin down the divinity which ensures that just so many people take up dentistry and just so many agree to milk the cows which would otherwise scream in pain just as children would scream if there were no dentists.

ALBERT: I see. A lunatic, in fact.

FRASER: Not certifiably so. By no means certified. I am simply open, wide open, to certain insights. I do not believe that there is anyone in control. There is the semblance of pattern—supply meeting demand, one-way streets, give and take, the presumption of return tickets, promises to pay the bearer on demand, etcetera—but there's nothing really holding it together. One is forced to recognize the arbitrariness of what we claim to be order. Somewhere there is a lynch pin, which, when removed, will collapse the whole monkey-puzzle. And I'm not staying there till it happens.

ALBERT: I see. Well, we all have our problems, but I don't see how that justifies you climbing about council property. So would you kindly descend——

FRASER: That's what I came up for.

ALBERT: To descend?

FRASER: It never occurred to me to stay.

ALBERT: You came up to go down?

FRASER: To jump.

ALBERT: Jump?

FRASER: Off.

ALBERT: Jump off? You'd kill yourself. Ah.

FRASER: Yes.

ALBERT: I scc. All right, then.

FRASER: My mind was made up——

ALBERT: I see your point.

FRASER: It seemed the easiest thing to do.

ALBERT: I agree. Well then, time is hurrying by, waiting for no man. Or is that tide?

FRASER: I see you're trying to humour me. Well, I expected that. You'll be sending for a priest next.

ALBERT: Come, come, don't procrastinate.

FRASER: Me?

ALBERT: You said you were going to jump.

FRASER: Well?

ALBERT: Well, jump.

FRASER: Aren't you going to try to talk me out of it?

ALBERT: You know your own mind. And you're holding me up. I've got to paint where you're standing.

FRASER: You wouldn't just stand there without lifting a finger?

ALBERT: I knew it. You're just a talker. Those ones never do it.

FRASER: I can't believe it. You wouldn't just stand there and watch me kill myself.

ALBERT: I thought that's what you wanted.

FRASER: Well, I did. I couldn't bear the noise, and the chaos. I couldn't get free of it, the enormity of that disorder, so dependent on a chance sequence of action and reaction. So I started to climb, to get some height, you know, enough height to drop from, to be sure, and the higher I climbed, the more I saw and the less I heard. And look now. I've been up here for hours, looking down and all it is, is dots and bricks, giving out a gentle hum. Quite safe. Quite

small after all. Quite ordered, seen from above. Laid out
in squares, each square a function, each dot a functionary.
I really think it might work. Yes, from a vantage point
like this, the idea of society is just about tenable.

ALBERT: Funked it. Well, mind how you go. Don't fall.

(*Cut bridge.*)

CHAIRMAN: Gentlemen. This special emergency meeting of the
Clufton Bay Bridge Sub-Committee has been called as a
result of public representations, both direct and via the
press, concerning the unsightly condition of what is the
symbol of Clufton's prosperity. My grandfather, who was
loved by the public, and owed everything to them, must be
turning in his grave. It is a salutary reminder that we are all
servants of the public, Mr. Fitch.

DAVE: Hear hear, Mr. Chairman.

CHAIRMAN: Shut up, Dave. As chairman, I, of course, take full
responsibility. That is the duty of the chairman, regardless
of where that responsibility actually lies, Mr. Fitch.

GEORGE: Hear hear, Mr. Chairman.

CHAIRMAN: It is no smiling matter, George. The city publicity
officer has been on to me, the Parks and Amenities have
been on to me, British Railways have been on to me and
the *Clufton Chronicle* has been doing its damndest to get on
to me. This committee is the shame and the laughing stock
of the Clufton Council, and as the future—as a possible
future Mayor, I am gravely embarrassed by having to carry
the can for a lack of foresight and watchfulness on the part
of committee members whose names I will not mention,
George. I have issued a statement to the effect that the
squalid state of disrepair of Clufton's highly-respected
bridge is the result of a miscalculation by a senior public
official, for which I, as chairman, take full responsibility,
Mr. Fitch.

FITCH (*a broken man*): I can only say in mitigation that I have
been under pressure—a sick man—domestic and financial
worries——

CHAIRMAN: Quite, quite. Let's stick to essentials. Two years ago, at your insistence and against my better judgement, which I left unspoken in deference to your professional capacity, we arranged to switch to improved paint lasting eight years, and through a reasoning which I never pretended to follow, to sack three of the four painters. Today, two years later, we are left with a bridge that is only one quarter painted while the other three-quarters is in a condition ranging from the sub-standard to the decrepit. Now then—what happened?

FITCH: Mr. Chairman, gentlemen, I have served Clufton man and boy for five years. . . . Clufton is the repository of my dreams and boyhood memories, the temple of my hopes to transform the running of a living community to a thing of precision and efficiency, a cybernetic poem—a programmed machine as perfect as a rose——

CHAIRMAN: For God's sake, Fitch, pull yourself together.

FITCH: Gentlemen, let us take as our starting point the proposition that X painters painting at the rate of Y would take Z years to paint surface ABC. We found that when X equalled four, Z equalled two, Y and ABC remaining constant. Then along came factor P, a paint lasting eight years——

CHAIRMAN: I can't stand it.

GEORGE: I think what Mr. Fitch is getting at Mr. Chairman is that the brown paint on the bridge was only supposed to last two years, the time that it took four painters to finish the job and start again. Well, of course, when we cut down to one painter using eight-year paint, it was obvious that in two years' time he'd only be a quarter of the way along, so the old paint would be ready for another coat.

CHAIRMAN: If it was obvious why didn't you say so?

GEORGE: I couldn't catch the eye of the chairman. Of course, if we could hang on for another six years, Mr. Fitch would emerge triumphantly vindicated as the poet of precision and efficiency.

CHAIRMAN: I might be dead in six years.

DAVE: Hear hear, Mr. Chairman.

CHAIRMAN: Thank you, Dave. So what are we going to do about it? Fitch?

FITCH: Er. . . . If we hired extra painters, one to start at the far
end, one in the middle going one way, another going the
opposite way, no . . . er, the progressive element intercedes
—if we have two painters back to back at a point nine-
sixteenths from the far end—no——

CHAIRMAN: We'd better go back to the old system and hire
three more painters. Carry on from there.

FITCH: You can't do that! They wouldn't be quick enough on
the one hand and they'd finish too soon on the other—you
see, the bridge won't need re-painting for another six years,
and the resultant coefficient—waste and unsightliness—the
entire system would disintegrate and cost thousands——

CHAIRMAN: Money? (*Appalled.*) My grandfather——

GEORGE: I think I see a way out, Mr. Chairman. From the
points of view of efficiency and expediency, I think we can
get the whole thing resolved with just a bit of organization.

FITCH: Every day counts.

GEORGE: One day is all we'll need.

(*Cut.*)


ALBERT: Met a feller up on the bridge the other day.

KATE (*strained*): Oh yes?

ALBERT: Yes. Climbed up to chuck himself off.

KATE: Did he?

ALBERT: No. Once he got up there, the mood passed.

KATE: Albert. . . .

ALBERT (*going*): Just off.

KATE: You used to say good-bye.


(*Cut to bridge.*)

FRASER: Hello.

ALBERT: Who's that?

FRASER: Me again.

ALBERT: Did you forget something?

FRASER: No, it all came back to me. After I went down, it all
started again. So I came back up.

ALBERT: To jump?

FRASER: Yes.

ALBERT: Go on then.

FRASER: I'm all right again now. I don't want to.

ALBERT: Now look here, this isn't a public right of way. I'll
report you.

FRASER: I can't help it. I'm forced up and coaxed down. I'm a
victim of perspective.

ALBERT (*shouts*): Get down!

FRASER: All right, I'm going.

(*Cut bridge.*)

ALBERT: I'm not a complaining man. I let people get on with
their own lives, I'm sympathetic to problems, but a line
must be drawn. I've found him up there four times now,
Mr. Fitch, and each time it's the same story—he doesn't
want to jump after all. I've given him every chance.

FITCH: Yes yes, but that isn't what I've asked to see you about
at all. You haven't been listening to me.

ALBERT: It's unnerving me, finding company up there. Well, it's
changing the character of the job, and playing hell with my
schedule—simply on the level of efficiency I protest.

FITCH: Well, as I say, for the reasons given, the matter is to be
resolved. We have to get the bridge finished by the end of
the week.

ALBERT: What?

FITCH: We can't allow further deterioration. The public is roused.

ALBERT: Wait a minute—I can't possibly finish by the end of
the week.

FITCH: I realize, of course, you'll need help. I have made
arrangements.

ALBERT: What arrangements?

FITCH: Eighteen-hundred painters will report for work at seven
o'clock tomorrow morning. By nightfall the job will be done.
I have personally worked it out, and my department has
taken care of the logistics.

ALBERT: Eighteen-hundred?

FITCH: Seventeen-hundred-and-ninety-nine. I kept a place for
you. I thought you'd like that.

(*Cut to door slam.*)

ALBERT (*breathless*): They're moving in on me, the dots are ganging up. I'll need food and spare clothes, a couple of blankets. What are you doing?

KATE (*off*): Packing, Albert. I'm going.

ALBERT: Kate, they've got it in for me. They're trying to move me off—and I've earned my position. I've worked for it.

KATE (*approach*): I've got a position—a housemaid, living in. With Katherine. I'll let you know my days off, for visiting. (*Pause.*)

ALBERT: Kate . . . I'm sorry. . . . Will you come and see me sometimes. . . . ? Will you come along and wave?


(*Cut in bridge and painting.*)
(*More rapid than before.*)
Dip brush, dip brush—slap it on, slide silver
over the iron, glide like mercury—slick, wipe
tickle it wet, swish, slop, sweep and wipe the
silver slime, it's all I can do—
in eight years I'll be pushing thirty-two
a manic painter coming through for the second time.
Dip brush, dip brush—

FRASER: What's the rush?

(*Painting stops.*)

ALBERT: Fraser.

FRASER: You're going at it.

ALBERT (*shouting*): Get down! Get down!

FRASER: This isn't like you at all.

ALBERT: I'm not having you up here.

FRASER: There's room for both of us.

ALBERT: You're just the first, and I'm not going to have it. If you're going to jump—jump.

FRASER: That's why I came, again.

ALBERT (*closer and quieter*): You're going to jump?

FRASER: No. Not today.

ALBERT (*furious*): Up and down like a yo-yo!

FRASER: I agree that it is ludicrous. Down there I am assailed by the flying splinters of a world breaking up at the speed of procreation without end. The centre cannot hold and the outside edge is filling out like a balloon, without the assurance of infinity. More men are hungry than honest, and more eat than produce. The apocalypse cannot be long delayed.

ALBERT: You'd be better out of it. I'll tell them why you did it, if that's what worrying you.

FRASER: . . . So I climb up again and prepare to cast myself off, without faith in angels to catch me—or desire that they should—and lo! I look down at it all and find that the proportions have been re-established. My confidence is restored, by perspective.

ALBERT: But it's my bridge——

FRASER: You think only of yourself—you see yourself as the centre, whereas I know that I am not placed at all——

ALBERT: There are other bridges—bigger——

FRASER (*listening*): What's that?

ALBERT: San Francisco—Sydney——

FRASER: Listen.

ALBERT: Brooklyn—there's a place for you——

FRASER: Listen!

ALBERT: —but I was here first—this is mine——

(*He tails off as there is the faintest sound of 1,800 men marching, whistling 'Colonel Bogey'.*)

FRASER: There's an army on the march. . . .

ALBERT: So they're coming. . . .

FRASER: A solid phalanx moving squarely up the road, an officer at the head. . . .

ALBERT: Fitch.

FRASER: But they're not soldiers.

ALBERT: He's mad.

FRASER (*appalled*): They're just—people.

ALBERT (*shouts—to the people*): Go away!

FRASER: Coming here.

ALBERT: Halt! About turn!

FRASER: They've lined up hundreds and hundreds of ordinary people—the overflow—all the fit men in the prime of life—they're always the ones on the list—preference is given to the old and the sick, the women and children—when it comes to the point, it's the young and able-bodied who go first——

ALBERT: Can't you see—they're taking over!

FRASER: Ten abreast—sixty deep—and another phalanx behind —and another—successive waves——

(*The whistling is getting louder.*)

—so it has come to this.

ALBERT: They're going to come up!

FRASER: It was the only direction left.

ALBERT: They're going to wheel right——

FITCH (*distant*): Right—wheel!

ALBERT: Off the road and through the gate——

FITCH: Straighten up there!

ALBERT: Up to the end of the bridge, on to the tracks——

FRASER: That's it, then—they have finally run out of space, the edges have all filled out and now there is only up.

ALBERT: Eighteen-hundred men—flung against me by a madman! Was I so important? Here they come.

(*This is difficult; as the front rank reaches the bridge, the tramp-tramp of the march should start to ring hollow, progressively as more and more leave terra firma and reach the bridge.*)

(*From now, approaching tears.*) I could have done it, given time——

FRASER: There will be more behind them—the concrete mixers churn and churn until only a single row of corn grows between two cities, and is finally ground between their walls. . . .

ALBERT: They didn't give me a fair chance—I would have worked nights——

FRASER: They'll all come following—women and children too— and those that are at the top will be pushed off like disgraced legionaires——

ALBERT: I had it under control—ahead of schedule——

FRASER: Ah well. But they should be breaking step.

(*Tramp tramp.*)

Like soldiers do when they come to a bridge——

ALBERT: I was all right—I was doing well——

FRASER: For the very good reason—

> (*Tramp tramp.*)

> that if they don't—

ALBERT: I was still young—fit—

FRASER: —the pressures cannot bounce—but build and have to break out—

> (*The rivets are starting to pop.*)

ALBERT: —good head for heights——

FRASER: —they don't know, or don't believe it, but the physical laws are inviolable—

> (*Cracking and wrenching.*)

ALBERT: What's happening?

FRASER: —and if you carry on like that, a bridge will shiver, the girders tensed and trembling for the release of the energy being driven through them—

ALBERT: —it's breaking up!

FRASER: —until the rivets pop—

ALBERT (*screams*): What are they doing to my bridge!

FRASER: —and a forty-foot girder moans like a Jew's harp—

> (*Twang.*)

> —and one's enough——

ALBERT: To go to such lengths! I didn't do them any harm! What did I have that they wanted?

> (*The bridge collapses.*)

# IF YOU'RE GLAD I'LL BE FRANK

*A play for radio*

*If You're Glad, I'll Be Frank* received its first production on the BBC Third Programme on 8th February 1966. The cast was as follows:

| | |
|---|---|
| 1ST PORTER | Brian Hewlett |
| MYRTLE TRELAWNEY | Isabel Rennie |
| MR. MORTIMER | Henry Stamper |
| MR. COURTENAY-SMITH | Noel Howlett |
| SIR JOHN | Alan Haines |
| LORD COOT | Austin Trevor |
| BERYL BLIGH | Eva Haddon |
| OPERATOR | Elizabeth Proud |
| IVY, a bus conductress | Barbara Mitchell |
| 2ND PORTER | Henry Stamper |

Produced by John Tydeman

*From her first words it is apparent that* GLADYS *is the* "TIM" *girl, and always has been.*

*As such, she has two columns to herself.*

*The right-hand column is for the Speaking Clock, and as such it is ostensibly continuous. But of course we hear her voice direct, not through a telephone unless otherwise indicated.*

*The left-hand column is for her unspoken thoughts, and of course this one has the dominant value.*

*It should be obvious in the script when her "Tim" voice is needed in the background as counterpoint, and when it should be drowned altogether by the rising dominance of her thoughts.*

*When her* "TIM" *voice intrudes again I have indicated this* not *by the actual words she uses, because the actual time she announces should be related to the number of minutes or seconds that have passed (i.e. depending on the pace of the broadcast) but by suggesting the* space of time *that her speaking voice should take up, and this appears in the script in this form: (3–4 seconds).*

GLADYS *operates the pips too, and these are indicated thus:* (PIP PIP PIP).

*Some of* GLADYS's *sustained passages fall into something halfway between prose and verse, and I have gone some way to indicate the rhythms by line-endings, but of course the effect should not be declamatory.*


### Scene 1

FRANK, *who turns out to be a bus driver, is heard dialling* "TIM".

> GLADYS (*through phone*): At the
> third stroke it will be eight
> fifty-nine precisely.

FRANK (*amazed disbelief*): It
can't be. . . .


(*Fearful hope*): It's
not. . . ?


(*Joy.*) It is! . . . *Gladys!*
It's my Gladys!
(*Fade.*)

(PIP PIP PIP.)

. . . At the third stroke it will
be eight fifty-nine and ten
seconds. . . .
(PIP PIP PIP.)

. . . At the third stroke it will
be eight fifty-nine and
twenty seconds. . . .
(PIP PIP PIP.)


## Scene 2

*Exterior mid traffic, Big Ben begins its nine a.m. routine. Cut to
interior: no traffic, Big Ben fainter.*

PORTER (*murmurs*): Nine o'clock. Here we go.
(*What happens is this:* MYRTLE, MORTIMER, COURTENAY-
SMITH, SIR JOHN *and the* FIRST LORD OF THE POST OFFICE
(LORD COOT) *enter from the street on the first, third, fifth,
seventh and ninth strokes of Big Ben respectively* (*the
second, fourth, sixth and eighth strokes being heard through
the closed door.*) *Each opening of the door lets in traffic
sound momentarily and amplifies Big Ben.*)
(*Street door.*)
PORTER: Morning, Mrs. Trelawney.
MYRTLE (*gay*): Hello, Tommy.
(*And out through door.*)
(*Street door.*)
PORTER: Morning, Mr. Mortimer.
MORTIMER (*tired*): Good morning, Tom.
(*And out through door.*)
(*Street door.*)

PORTER: Good morning, Mr. Courtenay-Smith.

C.-SMITH (*vague*): Morning, Mr. Thompson.

    (*And out through door.*)

    (*Street door.*)

PORTER: Good morning, Sir John.

SIR JOHN (*aloof*): Ah, Thompson. . . .

    (*And out through door.*)

    (*Street door.*)

PORTER: Good morning, my Lord.

1ST LORD: Morning, Tommy. (*Conspiratorial.*) Anything to report?

PORTER: All on schedule, my Lord.

1ST LORD: Jolly good.

    (*Through door.*)

MYRTLE: Good morning, your Lordship.

1ST LORD: Good morning, Mrs. Trelawney.

    (*Through door.*)

MORTIMER: Good morning, my Lord.

1ST LORD: Good morning, ah, Mortimer.

    (*Through door.*)

C.-SMITH: Good morning, Lord Coot.

1ST LORD: Good morning, Mr. Courtenay-Smith.

    (*Through door.*)

SIR JOHN: What ho, Cooty.

1ST LORD: Morning, Jack.

    (*Through door.*)

BERYL: Good morning, sir.

1ST LORD (*startled*): Who are you?

BERYL: I'm new.

    (*Pause.*)

1ST LORD: I thought I couldn't account for you. . . . New what?

BERYL: New secretary, sir . . . Miss Bligh. They sent me over from Directory Enquiries last night.

1ST LORD: I see. What happened to my old—to Miss—er——

BERYL: Apparently she cracked, sir, at 1.53 a.m. I came at once.

1ST LORD: That's the ticket. The Post Office never sleeps. Do you know the form round here?

BERYL: Well. . . .

1ST LORD: Quite simple. I'm the First Lord of the Post Office, of course. I'm responsible for the lot, with special attention to the Telephone Services, which are as follows—write them down——

UMP—dial-the-Test-score.

SUN—dial-the-weather.

POP—dial-a-pop.

BET—dial-the-racing-results.

GOD—dial-the-Bible-reading.

EAT—dial-a-recipe.

And so on, with many others, including the most popular and important of them all—TIM, dial-the-speaking-clock. We can't afford to lose track of time, or we'd be lost. Now, you see, we must keep a continuous check on all of them, because if you don't keep an eye on them they slide back. The strain is appalling, and the staffing problems monumental.

Shall we start checking, then? To begin with, synchronize our watches, and then check with TIM—ready? I make it just coming up to nine two and forty seconds. . . .

## Scene 3

*Follows straight on with the Time signal* (PIP PIP PIP).
*Heard direct, i.e. not through phone, as is* GLADYS *now.*

GLADYS:

. . . At the third stroke it will be nine two and fifty seconds. . . .
(PIP PIP PIP.)
. . . At the third stroke it will be nine three precisely.
(PIP PIP PIP.)

Or to put it another way, three minutes past nine, precisely, though which

nine in particular, I don't
say, so what's precise
about that? . . .

         . . . nine three and ten
         seconds. . . .
         (PIP PIP PIP.)

The point is beginning to be
   lost on me.
Or rather it is becoming a
   different point.
Or rather I am beginning
   to see through it.
Because they think that
   time is something they
   invented,
for their own convenience,
and divided up into ticks
   and tocks
and sixties and twelves
and twenty-fours . . .
so that they'd know when
   the Olympic record has
   been broken
and when to stop serving
   dinner in second-class
   hotels,
when the season opens and
   the betting closes,
when to retire;
when to leave the station,
renew their applications
when their subscriptions
   have expired;
when time has run out.
So that they'd know how
   long they lasted,
and pretend that it matters,
and how long they've got,

as if it mattered,
so that they'd know that we
    know that they know.
That we know, that is.
That they know, of course.

And so on.

(*Faint time clock, 2–3
seconds.*)

Ad infinitum.

I used to say ad nauseum
but it goes on long after you
    feel sick.
And I feel sick.
When you look down from
    a great height
you become dizzy. Such
    depth, such distance,
such disappearing tininess so
    far away,
rushing away,
reducing the life-size to
    nothing—
it upsets the scale you live by.
Your eyes go first, followed
    by the head,
and if you can't look away
    you feel sick.
And that's my view of time;
and I can't look away.
Dizziness spirals up between
    my stomach and my head
corkscrewing out the stopper
But I'm empty anyway.
I was emptied long ago.

Because it goes on,

this endless dividing up into
   equal parts,
this keeping track—
because time viewed from
   such distance
etcetera
rushing away
reducing the lifespan to
   nothing
and so on—
(*Pause.*)
The spirit goes first, followed
   by the mind.
And if you can't look away
   you go mad.

                  (*Time clock, 2–3 seconds.*)


### Scene 4

   FRANK *dialling; excited, intense. Ringing tone breaks off.*
OPERATOR *is heard through phone.*

OPERATOR: Number please.
FRANK: Listen, do all you people work in the same building?
OPERATOR: This is the operator—can I help you?
FRANK: I want to speak to Gladys Jenkins.
OPERATOR: What's the number, please?
FRANK: She works there—she's in the telephones, you see.
OPERATOR: Hello, sir—operator here——
FRANK: I want to be transferred to Mrs. Jenkins—this is her
   husband.
OPERATOR: Mrs. Jenkins?
FRANK: Speaking clock.
OPERATOR: Do you want to know the time?
FRANK: No—I want my Gladys! What's her number?
OPERATOR: Speaking clock?

FRANK: Yes.

OPERATOR: TIM.

FRANK: Her *number*.

OPERATOR: T-I-M.

FRANK: I demand to speak to your superior——

OPERATOR: Just a moment, sir, putting you through.

GLADYS (*through phone*): . . . At the third stroke it will be nine twelve and forty seconds. . . .

FRANK: It's all right, Glad—it's me again—Frank!

(GLADYS's *timespeak continues underneath.*)

Can you hear me now, Glad?—I've had a time of it I can tell you—I must say, you gave me a turn! So that's where you got to—Gladys? Give over a minute, love—it's Frank—— Can you hear me, Gladys? Give me a sign?

(*Pause; timeclock.*)

I know your voice—it's you, isn't it Gladys—are they holding you?—I'll get you out of there, Gladys—I'll speak to the top man—I'll get the wheels turning, Gladys! I'll pull the strings, don't you worry, love—— But I've got to dash now, love—I'm calling from the terminus and we're due out——

(IVY, *a bus conductress breaks in.*)

IVY: Frank *Jenkins!* The passengers are looking at their watches!

FRANK (*to* IVY): Just coming. (*To* GLADYS.) That was Ivy, my conductress—you don't know Ivy—I'm on a new route now, the 52 to Acton—— Keep your chin up, Glad—you can hear me can't you? I'll be giving you another ring later—— Good-bye, Gladys—oh, Gladys—what's the time now?

GLADYS: Nine fourteen precisely——

FRANK: Thanks, Glad—oh, *thank* you, Gladys! (*He rings off.*)

IVY (*off*): Frank—it's nine fourteen—remember the schedule!

FRANK (*going*): Hey, Ivy—I've found her—I've found my Gladys!

### Scene 5

GLADYS (*direct voice now*):

> ... At the third stroke
> it will be nine fourteen
> and twenty seconds. . . .
> (PIP PIP PIP.)

... At the third stroke ...
I don't think I'll bother, I
don't think there's any point.
Let sleeping dogs and so on.
Because I wouldn't shake it off
by going back, I'd only be in
the middle of it,
with an inkling of infinity,
the only one who has seen both
    ends
rushing away from the middle.
You can't keep your balance
    after that.
Because they don't know what
    time is.
They haven't experienced the
    silence
in which it passes
impartial disinterested
godlike.
Because they didn't invent it at all.
They only invented the clock.
And it doesn't go tick
and it doesn't go tock
and it doesn't go pip.
It doesn't go anything.
And it doesn't go anything for
    ever.
It just goes,
before them, after them, without
them,

above all without them,
and their dialling fingers,
their routine-checking, schedule-
    setting time-keeping clockwork—
luminous, anti-magnetic,
fifteen-jewelled self-winding,
grandfather, cuckoo, electric
shock-, dust- and waterproofed,
    chiming;
it counts for nothing against the
    scale of time,
and makes them tiny, bound and
    gagged to the minute-hand
as though across a railway line—
struggling without hope, eyes busy
    with silent-screen distress
as the hour approaches—the express
swings round the curve towards
    them
(and the Golden Labrador who
    might have saved them
never turns up on time).

                              *(2–3 seconds.)*

And they count for nothing
    measured against
the moment in which a glacier
    forms and melts.
Which does not stop them from
    trying
to compete;
they synchronize their watches,
count the beats,
to get the most out of the little
    they've got,
clocking in, and out,
and speeding up,
keeping up with their time-tables,
and adjusting their tables to keep

up with their speed,
and check one against the other
and congratulate each other—
a minute saved to make another
    minute possible somewhere else
to be spent another time.
Enough to soft-boil a third of an egg:
hard-boil a fifth.

Precisely. . . .
(PIP PIP PIP.)
(*3–4 seconds.*)

Of course, it's a service if you like.
They dial for twenty second's worth
    of time
and hurry off contained within it
until the next correction,
with no sense of its enormity, none,
no sense of their scurrying
    insignificance;
only the authority of my voice,
the voice of the sun itself,
more accurate than Switzerland—
definitive
divine.

(*2–3 seconds, very faint.*)

If it made a difference
I could refuse to play,
sabotage the whole illusion
a little every day if it made a
    difference,
as if it would, if I coughed or
    jumped a minute
(they'd correct their watches by my
    falter).
And if I stopped to explain
At the third stroke it will be

At the third stroke it
will be. . . . (*Continues
3–4 seconds.*)

too late to catch up, far
far too late, gentlemen. . . .
they'd complain, to the Post Office
And if stopped altogether,
just stopped, gave up the pretence,
it would make no difference.
Silence is the sound of time passing.

*(1–2 seconds, faint.)*

Don't ask when the pendulum
    began to swing.
Because there is no pendulum.
It's only the clock that goes tick
    tock
and never the time that chimes.
It's never the time that stops.

*(1–2 seconds, quick fade.)*

### Scene 6

VOICE THROUGH PHONE: . . . thirty minutes in a Regulo 5 oven
    until it is a honey coloured brown. . . . Serves six.
1ST LORD *(ringing off)*: Well, that's that one. Next.
BERYL: That was the last one, sir.
1ST LORD: Then start again at the beginning—continuous
    attention, you see. You'll have to take over this afternoon
    —I have a board meeting.
BERYL: Very good, sir.
1ST LORD: You don't have to call me sir. Call me my Lord.
BERYL: Very good, my Lord.
    *(Phone rings.)*
    Hello?
FRANK *(through phone)*: This is Frank Jenkins.
BERYL: Yes?
FRANK: It's about my wife.
BERYL: Yes?
FRANK: Is she there?

BERYL: This is the First Lord's office.

FRANK: I want the top man in speaking clocks.

BERYL: What name please?

FRANK: Jenkins—it's about my wife, Gladys. She's the speaking clock.

BERYL: Hold on, please.
My Lord, it's a Mr. Jenkins—he says his wife is the speaking clock.

1ST LORD: How extraordinary. Tell him we don't know what he's talking about.

*Scene 7*

GLADYS (*direct*):

    ... At the third stroke
it will be eleven thirty
precisely. ...
(PIP PIP PIP.)

Old Frank. ...
Yes, we met dancing, I liked him
   from the first.
He said, "If you're Glad
I'll be Frank. ..."
There was time to laugh then
but while I laughed a bumblebee
fluttered its wings a million times.
How can one compete?
His bus passed my window twice a day,
on the route he had then,
every day, with a toot and a wave
   and was gone.
toot toot toot
everything the same
if only you didn't know,
which I didn't
which I do.
He took his timetable seriously,
   Frank.

You could set your clock by him.
But not *time*—it flies by
unrepeatable
and the moment after next the
    passengers are dead
and the bus scrap and the scrap dust,
caught by the wind, blown into the
    crevasse
as the earth splits and scatters
at the speed of bees wings.
Old Frank. He had all the time
in the world for me,
such as it was.

                              (PIP PIP PIP.)


### Scene 8


*In the street* FRANK's *bus comes to a rather abrupt halt, the door of his cab opens, slams shut as he runs across the pavement and through a door. He is breathless and in a frantic hurry.*

FRANK: Hey, you—who's in charge here?
PORTER: I am. Is that your bus?
FRANK: Who's the top man—quick!
PORTER: You can't park there after seven if the month's got an R in it or before nine if it hasn't except on Christmas and the Chairman's birthday should it fall in Lent.
FRANK: I have an appointment with the chairman.
PORTER (*to the sound of horns*): Seems to be a bit of a traffic jam out there.
FRANK: What floor's he on?
PORTER: He's not on the floor this early. Is this your conductress?
   (*As the door flies open.*)
IVY: Frank—what are you doing!
FRANK: All right, all right! (*To* PORTER.) Listen—I'll be passing your door again at one-fourteen. Tell him to be ready——

CONDUCTRESS: Frank—we'll get behind time!

FRANK (*Leaving hurriedly*): It's all right, I got ninety seconds ahead going round the park. . . .
(*And out; and break.*)


### Scene 9


*In the street* FRANK'*s bus draws up once more; same slam, same feet, same door, same frenzy.*


FRANK: Where is he? I've got ninety-five seconds.

2ND PORTER: Who?

FRANK: Who are you?

2ND PORTER: What do you want?

FRANK: Where's the other porter?

2ND PORTER: Gone to lunch—it's one-fourteen.

FRANK: Never mind him—where's the chairman?

2ND PORTER: They eat together.
(*Door crashes open.*)

CONDUCTRESS: Frank *Jenkins!*

2ND PORTER: Like brothers.

CONDUCTRESS: What about the schedule!?

FRANK (*to* PORTER): Listen—I'll be back here at two forty-seven——

CONDUCTRESS (*almost in tears*): I ask you to remember the schedule!

2ND PORTER (*as the horns sound*): Hello—is that your bus out there?

FRANK (*leaving hurriedly*): Two forty-seven!—tell him it's about Gladys Jenkins!


### Scene 10


GLADYS (*through phone*): . . . three fourteen and twenty seconds. . . .
(PIP PIP PIP.)

1ST LORD (*ringing off*): Precisely! Next!
BERYL: God, my Lord.
GOD (*through phone*): In the beginning was the Heaven and the
   Earth. . . .
   (*Fade.*)


*Scene 11*


GLADYS (*direct*):                                    . . . At the third stroke
                                                     it will be three fourteen
                                                     and fifty seconds. . . .

   Check, check, check. . . .
   One day I'll give him something
   to check up for . . .
   tick tock
   tick tock
   check check
   chick chock
   tick
   you can check
   your click clock
   by my pip pip pip                                 (PIP PIP PIP.)
   I never waver,
   I'm reliable,
   lord, lord,
   I'm your servant,
   trained,
   precisely.                                        . . . precisely.
   (*With a click* FRANK *is on the line.*)
   (*We hear him, as* GLADYS *does, through the phone.*)
FRANK: Hello, Gladys—it's Frank. I bet you wondered where
   I'd got to. . . . Well, I've had a bit of trouble getting hold
   of the right man, you see, but don't you worry because the
   next trip will give me the time—I'll be bang outside his
   door slap in the middle of the rush hour so I'll have a
   good four minutes—can you hear me, Gladys? . . .
   (*Breaks a little.*)

Oh, Gladys—talk to me—I want you back, I'll let you do
anything you like if you come back—I'll let you be a nun,
if that's what you really want . . . Gladys? I love you,
Gladys——
Hold on, love, hold on a bit, and I'll have you out of
there. . . .
Got to go now, Gladys, Ivy's calling me, we're due out.
Bye bye . . . bye bye. . . . (*Rings off.*)

GLADYS:

I can hear them all
though they do not know enough to
speak to me.
I can hear them breathe,
pause, listen,
sometimes the frogsong of clockwindings
and the muttered repetition to the
nearest minute . . .
but never a question of a question,
never spoken,
it remains open, permanent,
demanding a different answer
every ten seconds.

Until Frank.
Oh, Frank, you knew my voice,
but how can I reply?
I'd bring the whole thing down with a cough,
stun them with a sigh. . . .
(*Sobbing a little.*)
I was going to be a nun, but they wouldn't have me
because I didn't believe, I didn't believe *enough*, that is;
most of it I believed all right, or was willing to believe,
but not enough for their purposes, not about him being
the son of God, for instance, that's the part that put paid
to my ambition, that's where we didn't see eye to eye.
No, that's one of the main points, she said, without that
you might as well believe in a pair of old socks for all the
good you are to us, or words to that effect. I asked her to

stretch a point but she wasn't having any of it. I asked her
to let me stay inside without being a proper nun, it made
no difference to me, it was the serenity I was after, that and
the clean linen, but she wasn't having any of that.
(*Almost a wail.*)
But it's not the same thing at all!
I thought it would be—peace!
Oh, Frank—tell them—
I shan't go on, I'll let go
and sneeze the fear of God into
their alarm-setting, egg-timing,
train-catching, coffee-breaking
    faith in
an uncomprehended clockwork—

yes, if I let go,
lost track
changed the beat, went off the rails—
cracked——

... At the third stroke it
will be three eighteen
and ten seconds. . . .
(PIP PIP PIP.)

At the third stroke
it will be
three eighteen and
twenty seconds. . . .
And so what?

At the third stroke
it will be
three eighteen and
twenty seconds. . . .
(PIP PIP PIP.)

At the third stroke
it will be
too late to do any good,
gentlemen——

At the third stroke
it will be
three eighteen and thirty
seconds. . . .
(PIP PIP PIP.)
At the third stroke. . . .

At the third stroke
Manchester City 2,
Whores of Lancashire 43 for
seven declared

At the third stroke
Sheffield Wednesday will be cloudy
and so will Finisterre. . . .
(*The Queen.*) So a Merry Christmas
and God Bless you everywhere. . . .
And now the Prime Minister! :
Gentlemen, the jig is up—I have
given you tears. . . .
And now the First Lord!—
Don't lose your heads while all
about you on the burning deck. . . .
*Oh—Frank!* Help me! . . .

## Scene 12

FRANK'*s bus stops abruptly. Same place, same slam, same feet,
same door, same frenzy.*

FRANK : Right, let's not waste time—where is she?
PORTER : State your business.
FRANK : I'm looking for my wife.
PORTER : Name?
FRANK : Jenkins—you know me.
PORTER : *Her* name!
FRANK : Sorry—Jenkins.
PORTER : Better. Your name?
FRANK : Jenkins.
PORTER : Relative?
FRANK : Husband.
PORTER : Holds water so far.
FRANK : I demand to see your superior.
PORTER : Name?
FRANK : Jenkins!
PORTER : No one of that name here.
FRANK : I see your game—a conspiracy, is it?
PORTER (*as the horns sound*) : Is that your bus out there?

FRANK: I demand to speak to the chief of speaking clocks.

PORTER (*as the door bursts open*): Here she comes.

IVY (*conductress*): I'm not covering up for you again, Frank Jenkins!

PORTER: Hey—you can't go in there!

(*Door.*)

MYRTLE: Hello.

FRANK: Where's the top man?

MYRTLE: Keep on as you're going.

(*Door.*)

MORTIMER: Who are you?

FRANK: I want my wife!

MORTIMER: Now, look here, old man, there's a time and place for everything——

FRANK: I want her back!

MORTIMER: My dear fellow, please don't make a scene in the office——

FRANK: You're holding her against her will——

MORTIMER: I think that's for her to say. The fact is Myrtle and I are in love——

FRANK: I want my Gladys.

MORTIMER: Gladys? Isn't your name Trelawney?

FRANK: Jenkins—where's my Gladys?

MORTIMER: Gladys?

FRANK: My wife——

MORTIMER: Are you suggesting that a man of my scrupulous morality——

(*Door.*)

MYRTLE: Darling, there's a bus conductress outside——

MORTIMER: Thank you, Mrs. Trelawney——

IVY (*desperate*): Frank!—the traffic is beginning to move!

FRANK: I demand to see your superior!

MORTIMER: You can't go in there!

(*Door.*)

C.-SMITH: Yes?

FRANK: Are you the top man?

MORTIMER: Excuse me, Mr. Courtenay-Smith, this man just burst into——

IVY: Frank—I ask you to think of your schedule!

FRANK: Shut up! You there, are you the top man?

C.-SMITH: In my field, or do you speak hierarchically?

FRANK: I speak of Gladys Jenkins.

C.-SMITH: Not my field——

FRANK: You've got my wife——

MORTIMER: How dare you suggest that a man of Mr.
   Courtenay-Smith's scrupulous morality——

IVY: Frank! the passengers have noticed!
   (*Door.*)

C.-SMITH: Where's he gone?

MYRTLE: Darling, what's going on?

MORTIMER: Mrs. Trelawney, I must ask you to address me——

C.-SMITH: My God—the time-and-motion system won't take
   the strain!

IVY (*fading*): Fra-a-a-nk. . . !


### Scene 13


GLADYS (*breaking down slowly but surely*):

At the third stroke
I'm going to give it up,
yes, yes . . . it's asking too much,
for one person to be in the know
of so much, for so many . . .
and at the third stroke
Frank will come
. . . Frank. . . .
I'm going to drop it now,
it can go on without me,
and it will,
time doesn't need me—
they think I'm time, but I'm
not—
I'm Gladys Jenkins and at the
   third stroke

At the third stroke it
will be four twenty-
three and ten
seconds. . . .

I'm going to cough,
sneeze
whisper an obscenity that will leave
ten thousand coronaries sprawled
across their telephone tables,
and the trains will run half empty
and all the bloody eggs will turn to
volcanic rock smoking in dry
    cracked saucepans
as soon as I shout—
*Ship!*
(a vessel)
*Pis*cine!
(pertaining to fishes)
*Fruc!*tuate
(fruit-bearing)
(*She giggles hysterically.*)
oh yes I will
and then they'll let me go
they'll have to
because Frank knows I'm here—
come on, please Frank, I love you
and at the third stroke I will
yes I will yes at the third stroke I
    will. . . .


*Scene 14*

1ST LORD: Well, gentlemen, in bringing this board meeting to a
    close, and I'm sure you're all as bored as I am,
    (*Chuckle chuckle, hear hear.*)
    I think we must congratulate ourselves on the variety and
    consistency of the services which we in the telephone office
    have maintained for the public in the face of the most
    difficult problems. I believe I'm right in saying that if the
    last Test Match had not been abandoned because of the

rain, UMP would barely have lasted the five days, but all
was well as it happened, though the same rainy conditions
did put an extra strain on SUN our weather forecast
service. . . . I don't know if you have anything to add, Sir
John?

SIR JOHN: Well, Cooty—my Lord, that is—only to join with the
rest of the Board in heartily congratulating you on the
excellent report——

(*Hear hear hear hear.*)

1ST LORD: Thank you. Now is there any other business?

(*Door.*)

FRANK (*out of breath*): Where's Gladys Jenkins?!

1ST LORD: There you have me, gentlemen.

SIR JOHN: Point of order, my Lord.

1ST LORD: Yes, Jack?

SIR JOHN: I don't think this man——

FRANK: I'm not taking any more of this—where've you got my
Glad——

(*Door.*)

C.-SMITH: Forgive me, my Lord—this man is quite
unauthorized——

IVY: Frank, the passengers are rioting! All is lost!

MORTIMER: Now look here——

MYRTLE: Darling, do shut up!

FRANK: Damn you. What have you done with my wife?

SIR JOHN: Don't you come here with your nasty little
innuendoes, Trelawney—whatever you may have heard
about the Bournemouth conference, Myrtle and I——

IVY: The passengers are coming!

(FIRST LORD *gets quiet by banging his gavel.*)

(*Pause.*)

(*Noise of rioting passengers.*)

1ST LORD: Gentlemen—please! (*Pause.*) Now what's all the row
about?

IVY: It's the passengers, sir.

FRANK: Are you the top man?

1ST LORD: Certainly.

FRANK: What have you done with my Gladys?

MORTIMER: How dare you suggest that a man of the First Lord's scrupulous morality——

1ST LORD: Please, Mr. Mortimer, let him finish.

FRANK: She's the speaking clock.

1ST LORD: What do you mean? *TIM?*

FRANK: Gladys. Yes.

1ST LORD (*chuckling*): My dear fellow—there's no Gladys—we wouldn't trust your wife with the *time*—it's a machine, I thought everyone knew that. . . .

FRANK: A machine?

1ST LORD: He thought it was his wife!

(*General chuckles.*)

Wife . . . thought it was his wife! . . .

FRANK: It was her voice——

IVY: Oh, Frank—they wouldn't use your Glad for that. It's just the speaking clock——

FRANK: She was educated——

IVY: Oh Frank—come on, come on now, we'll be in awful trouble with the Inspector.

FRANK: But Ivy—she *talked* to me. . . .

IVY: She couldn't have done——

1ST LORD: She *talked* to you, my dear fellow?

FRANK: Well, not exactly. . . .

IVY: Of course she didn't. Come on, now. . . .

1ST LORD: That's it—back to your offices gentlemen. We must all make up for lost time.

(*General movement out.*)

FRANK: But she sounded like my Gladys. . . .

IVY: You'll have to go on looking, Frank. . . .

(FIRST LORD *alone.*)

1ST LORD: Dear me, dear me. . . .

(*Door.*)

BERYL (*urgent*): Sir!

1ST LORD: What is it, Miss Bligh?

BERYL: It's the speaking clock—I was just checking it and——

1ST LORD: All right—get me TIM, I'll see to it.

BERYL: Yes, my Lord. (*Dialling.*) She's on now, my Lord.

GLADYS (*through phone. Sobbing hysterically*): At the third

stroke it will be five thirty five and fifty seconds. . . .
(PIP PIP PIP.)

1ST LORD: Mrs. Jenkins. . . . This is the First Lord speaking.

GLADYS: At the third stroke it will be five thirty-six
precisely. . . .

1ST LORD: Mrs. Jenkins—pull yourself together, stop crying.
And you've lost forty seconds somewhere by my watch——

GLADYS: At the third stroke I don't know what time it is and I
don't care, because it doesn't go tick tock at all, it just
goes and I have seen—I have seen infinity!

1ST LORD: *Mrs. Jenkins!*

GLADYS (*sniffing*): I can't go on!

1ST LORD: Come on now, this isn't like you at all. Let's get
things back on the rails, hm? Think of the public, Mrs.
Jenkins. . . . Come on now . . . at the third stroke. . . .

GLADYS: At the third stroke. . . .

1ST LORD: It will be five thirty seven and forty seconds.
(PIP PIP PIP.)
Carry on from there. . . .

GLADYS: At the third stroke it will be five thirty-seven and
fifty seconds. . . .

1ST LORD: That's it—spot on Mrs. Jenkins. Control your voice
now.
(PIP PIP PIP.)

GLADYS: At the third stroke it will be five thirty-eight
precisely.

1ST LORD: Well done, Mrs. Jenkins. Well done—I'll check you
again within the hour, as usual. (*Rings off.*)

GLADYS (*direct now*):

He thinks he's God. . . .

At the third stroke it
will be five thirty-eight
and ten seconds. . . .
(PIP PIP PIP.)
At the third stroke. . . .
(*Fading out.*)

# ARTIST DESCENDING A STAIRCASE

*A play for radio*

**Note**

There are eleven scenes. The play begins in the here-and-now; the next five scenes are each a flashback from the previous scene; the seventh, eighth, ninth, tenth and eleventh scenes are, respectively, continuations of the fifth, fourth, third, second and first. So the play is set temporally in six parts, in the sequence ABCDEFEDCBA

A = here and now
B = a couple of hours ago
C = Last week
D = 1922
E = 1920
F = 1914

*Artist Descending a Staircase* received its first production on BBC Radio 3 on 14th November, 1972. The cast was as follows:

| | |
|---|---|
| MARTELLO (SENIOR) | Stephen Murray |
| BEAUCHAMP (SENIOR) | Rolf Lefebvre |
| DONNER (SENIOR) | Carleton Hobbs |
| SOPHIE | Fiona Walker |
| MARTELLO (JUNIOR) | Michael Spice |
| BEAUCHAMP (JUNIOR) | Peter Egan |
| DONNER (JUNIOR) | Dinsdale Landen |

Produced by John Tydeman

*We hear, on a continuous loop of tape, a sequence of sounds which is to be interpreted by* MARTELLO *and* BEAUCHAMP *thus:*

   (*a*) DONNER *dozing: an irregular droning noise.*

   (*b*) *Careful footsteps approach. The effect is stealthy. A board creaks.*

   (*c*) *This wakes* DONNER, *i.e. the droning stops in mid-beat.*

   (*d*) *The footsteps freeze.*

   (*e*) DONNER'*s voice, unalarmed:* 'Ah! There you are . . .'

   (*f*) *Two more quick steps, and then Thump!*

   (*g*) DONNER *cries out.*

   (*h*) *Wood cracks as he falls through a balustrade.*

   (*i*) *He falls heavily down the stairs, with a final sickening thump when he hits the bottom. Silence.*

*After a pause, this entire sequence begins again . . . Droning . . . Footsteps . . . (as before).*

MARTELLO: I think this is where I came in.

   (TAPE: '*Ah! There you are . . .*')

BEAUCHAMP: And this is where you hit him.

   (TAPE: *Thump!*)

MARTELLO: I *mean*, it's going round again. The tape is going round in a *loop*.

BEAUCHAMP: Well, of course. I record in loops, lassoing my material—no, like trawling—no, like—no matter.

   (TAPE: DONNER *reaches the bottom of the stairs.*)

MARTELLO: Poor Donner.

   (MARTELLO *and* BEAUCHAMP *are old men, as was* DONNER.

   (*The* TAPE *starts off again as before.*)

BEAUCHAMP (*over* TAPE): Round and round, recording layer upon layer of silence while Donner dozed after a heavy lunch, the

spools quietly folding silence upon itself, yes like packing
linen into trunks . . . Fold, fold until the footsteps broke
it . . . and woke him——
(TAPE: '*Ah! There you are . . .*')
How peaceful it was, in the afternoon in the great houses
before the Great War, to doze after luncheon with only a fly
buzzing in the stuffy room and a sense of the maids somewhere quietly folding the linen into pine chests . . .
(TAPE: DONNER *reaches the bottom of the stairs.*)
Donner knew the post-prandial nap. His people were
excellently connected. With mine, in fact.
(TAPE: *re-continues under.*)
I suppose we should let someone know, though not
necessarily the entire circumstances. I'm not one to tell
tales if no good can come of it.

MARTELLO: I will stand by you, Beauchamp. We have been
together a long time.

BEAUCHAMP: You may rely on me, Martello. I shall not cast the
first stone.

MARTELLO: You *have* cast it, Beauchamp, but I do not prejudge
you.

BEAUCHAMP: My feelings precisely, but there seems to be some
confusion in your mind——

MARTELLO: My very thought. Turn off your machine, it seems to
be disturbing your concentration——
(TAPE: '*Ah!*——' *and is switched off.*)

BEAUCHAMP: There you are.

MARTELLO: On the contrary, Beauchamp, there *you* are. Unless
we can agree on *that*, I can't even begin to help you clear
up this mess.

BEAUCHAMP: Don't touch him, Martello.

MARTELLO: I don't mean clear up *Donner!*—honestly, Beauchamp,
you buffoon!

BEAUCHAMP: Cynic!

MARTELLO: Geriatric!

BEAUCHAMP: Murderer!
(*Pause.*)

MARTELLO: As I was saying, I shall help you so far as I can

to get through the difficult days ahead, whether in duplicity
or in the police courts, depending on how you intend to
face the situation; but I shall do so only on the condition
that we drop this farce of accusation and counter-
accusation. You had only two friends in the world, and
having killed one you can't afford to irritate the other.

BEAUCHAMP: Very well!—I gave you your chance, and now I'm
going to get the police.

MARTELLO: A very sensible decision. You are too feeble to run, and
too forgetful to tell lies consistent with each other.
Furthermore, you are too old to make the gain worth the
trouble. Be absolutely frank with them, but do not plead
insanity. That would reflect undeserved credit on three
generations of art critics.

BEAUCHAMP: I must say, Martello, I have to admire your gall.

MARTELLO: Stress all mitigating factors, such as Donner's refusal
to clean the bath after use, and his infuriating mannerisms
any of which might have got him murdered years ago.
Remember how John used to say, 'If Donner whistles the
opening of Beethoven's Fifth in six/eight time once more I'll
*kill him!*'?

BEAUCHAMP: John who?

MARTELLO: Augustus John.

BEAUCHAMP: No, no, it was Edith Sitwell.

MARTELLO: Rubbish!—you're getting old, Beauchamp.

BEAUCHAMP: I am two years younger than you, Martello.

MARTELLO: Anybody who is two years younger than me is *senile*.
It is only by a great effort of will that my body has not
decomposed. Which reminds me, you can't leave Donner
lying there at the bottom of the stairs for very long in this
weather, and that is only the practical argument; how long
can you *ethically* leave him?

BEAUCHAMP: It is nothing to do with me.

MARTELLO: Beauchamp, I am shocked. You were at school
together. You signed his first manifesto, as he signed yours.
You have conjured with his name and travelled on his
ticket; shared his roof, his prejudices, his occasional grant;
eaten his bread and drunk his health (God forgive my

*brain!*—it is so attuned to the ironic tone it has become
ironical in repose; I have to whip sincerity out of it as one
whips responses from a mule!)—to put it plain, you have
been friends for over sixty years.

BEAUCHAMP: Well, the same goes for you.

MARTELLO: Yes, but you killed him.

BEAUCHAMP: I did no such thing!, and you have good reason to
know it! I am thoroughly disillusioned in you, Martello. I
was willing to bend over backwards to see your side of it,
but I can't stand a chap who won't come clean when he's
found out.

MARTELLO: I, on the other hand, admire your hopeless per-
sistence. But the tape recorder speaks for itself. That is, of
course, the point about tape recorders. In this case it is
eloquent, grandiloquent, not to say Grundigloquent—Oh
God, if only I could turn it *off!*—no wonder I have achieved
nothing with my life!—my brain is on a flying trapeze that
outstrips all the possibilities of action. Mental acrobatics,
Beauchamp—I have achieved nothing but mental acrobatics
—*nothing!*—whereas you, however wrongly and for whatever
reason, came to grips with life at least this once, and killed
Donner.

BEAUCHAMP: It's not true, Martello!

MARTELLO: Yes, yes, I tell you, *nothing!*—Niente! Nada!
Nichts!—Oh, a few pieces here and there, a few scandals—
Zurich—Paris—Buenos Aires—but, all in all, nothing, not
even among the nihilists! (*Pause.*) I tell you, Beauchamp, it's
no secret between us that I never saw much point in your
tonal art. I remember saying to Sophie, in the early days
when you were still using gramophone discs, Beauchamp is
wasting his time, I said, there'll be no revelations coming out
of *that*; no truth. And the critics won't listen either. And they
didn't. But this time you've got them by the ears. It has the
impact of newsreel. In my opinion it's a *tour de force*.

BEAUCHAMP: You are clearly deranged. It is probably the first time
a murderer has tried to justify himself on artistic grounds. As
it happens, you are also misguided. Far from creating a *tour
de force*, you ruined what would have been a strand in my

masterwork of accumulated silence, and left in its place a melodramatic fragment whose point will not be lost on a jury.

(*He presses* TAPE *switch:* '—*There you are*——' *etc.*)

There indeed he is, ladies and gentlemen, caught by the fortuitous presence of a recording machine that had been left running in the room where Mr. Donner was quietly working on a portrait from memory, a portrait fated to be unfinished.

MARTELLO: Poor Donner, he never had much luck with Sophie.

BEAUCHAMP: For the existence of this recording we have to thank Mr. Beauchamp, a fact which argues his innocence, where it ever in doubt. Mr. Beauchamp, an artist who may be familiar to some of you——

MARTELLO: If you are extremely old and collect trivia——

BEAUCHAMP: —and his friends, Mr. Donner and the man Martello, lived and worked together in a single large attic studio approached by a staircase, which led upwards from the landing, and was guarded at the top by an insubstantial rail, through which, as you will hear, Mr. Donner fell.

MARTELLO: An accident, really.

BEAUCHAMP: If you say so.

MARTELLO: You didn't mean to *kill* him. It was manslaughter.

BEAUCHAMP: You will hear how Mr. Donner, while working, dozed off in his chair . . .

(TAPE: *Droning.*)

Footsteps approach.

(TAPE: *Footsteps.*)

Someone has entered quietly. Who? No visitors came to this place. Martello and Mr. Beauchamp met their acquantances outside, formerly at the Savage, lattery in public houses. And Mr. Donner, who was somewhat reclusive, not to say misanthropic, had no friends at all—except the other two, *a fact whose importance speaks for itself*——

(TAPE: '*Ah! There you are* . . .'—*and is switched off.*)

Not, 'Who the devil are you?', or 'Good Lord, what are you doing here, I haven't seen you for donkey's years!'—no. 'Ah. there you are.' The footsteps can only have belonged to the man Martello.

MARTELLO: Or, or course, the man Beauchamp. I don't see where this is getting us—we already know perfectly well that it was *one* of us, and it is absurd that you should prevaricate in this way when there is no third party to impress. I came home to find Donner dead, and you at the top of the stairs, fiddling with your tape-recorder. It is quite clear that I arrived just in time to stop you wiping out the evidence.

BEAUCHAMP: But it was *I* who came home and found Donner dead —with your footsteps on the machine. My first thought was to preserve any evidence it had picked up, so I very quietly ascended——

MARTELLO: Beauchamp, why are you bothering to lie to *me?* You are like a man on a desert island refusing to admit to his only companion that he ate the last coconut.

BEAUCHAMP: For the very good reason that while my back was turned you shinned up the tree and guzzled it. And *incidentally*—I see that you have discovered where I keep my special marmalade. That's *stealing*, Martello, common theft. That marmalade does *not* come out of the house-keeping——

MARTELLO: It must have been Donner.

BEAUCHAMP: It was not Donner. Donner never cleaned the tub and he always helped himself to cheese in such a way as to leave all the rind, but he never stole my marmalade because he didn't *like* marmalade. He did steal my *honey*, I know that for a fact. And he had the nerve to accuse me of taking the top off the milk.

MARTELLO: Well, you do.

BEAUCHAMP (*furiously*): Because I have paid the milkman four weeks running! It's *my milk!*

MARTELLO: I suppose we should leave a note for him. Two pints a day will be enough now.

BEAUCHAMP: Since you will be in jail, one pint will be ample. Poor Donner. He was not so easy to get on with in recent years, but I shall always regret that my last conversation with him was not more friendly.

MARTELLO: Were you rowing about the housekeeping again?

BEAUCHAMP: No, no. He was rather unfeeling about my work in progress, as a matter of fact.

MARTELLO: He was rude about mine the other day. He attacked it.

BEAUCHAMP: He said mine was rubbish.

MARTELLO: Did he attack you? Was that it?

BEAUCHAMP: Why did he resent me? He seemed embittered, lately . . .

MARTELLO: He'd been brooding about Sophie.

BEAUCHAMP: And that ridiculous painting. What was the matter with the man?

MARTELLO: I think I was rather at fault . . .

BEAUCHAMP: I paid him the compliment of letting him hear how my master-tape was progressing . . .

## Flashback

(BEAUCHAMP's 'master-tape' is a bubbling cauldron of squeaks, gurgles, crackles, and other unharmonious noises. He allows it to play for longer than one would reasonably hope.)

BEAUCHAMP: Well, what do you think of it, Donner? Take your time, choose your words carefully.

DONNER: I think it's rubbish.

BEAUCHAMP: Oh. You mean, a sort of tonal debris, as it were?

DONNER: No, rubbish, general rubbish. In the sense of being worthless, without value; rot, nonsense. Rubbish, in fact.

BEAUCHAMP: Ah. The detritus of audible existence, a sort of refuse heap of sound . . .

DONNER: I mean, *rubbish*. I'm sorry, Beauchamp, but you must come to terms with the fact that our paths have diverged. I very much enjoyed my years in that child's garden of easy victories known as the avant garde, but I am now engaged in the infinitely more difficult task of painting what the eye sees.

BEAUCHAMP: Well, I've never seen a naked woman sitting about a garden with a unicorn eating the roses.

DONNER: Don't split hairs with *me*, Beauchamp. You don't know what art is. Those tape recordings of yours are the mechanical expression of a small intellectual idea, the kind

of notion that might occur to a man in his bath and be
forgotten in the business of drying between his toes. You
can call it art if you like, but it is the commonplace of any
ironic imagination, and there are thousands of clerks and
shop assistants who would be astonished to be called artists
on their bath night.

BEAUCHAMP: Wait a minute, Donner——

DONNER: And they, incidentally, would call your tapes——

BEAUCHAMP: Quiet!——

DONNER: —rubbish.

(*Smack!*)

BEAUCHAMP: Missed him! I don't want that fly buzzing around
the microphone—I'm starting up a new loop.

DONNER: I see I'm wasting my breath.

BEAUCHAMP: I heard you. Clerks—bath-night—rubbish, and so
on. But my tapes are not for clerks. They are for initiates, as
is all art.

DONNER: My kind is for Everyman.

BEAUCHAMP: Only because every man is an initiate of that
particular mystery. But your painting is not for dogs,
parrots, bicycles . . . You select your public. It is the same
with me, but my tapes have greater mystery—they elude
dogs, parrots, clerks and the greater part of mankind. If you
played my tape on the radio, it would seem a meaningless
noise, because it fulfils no expectations: people have been
taught to expect certain kinds of insight but not others. The
first duty of the artist is to capture the radio station.

DONNER: It was Lewis who said that.

BEAUCHAMP: Lewis who?

DONNER: Wyndham Lewis.

BEAUCHAMP: It was Edith Sitwell, as a matter of fact.

DONNER: Rubbish.

BEAUCHAMP: She came out with it while we were dancing.

DONNER: You never danced with Edith Sitwell.

BEAUCHAMP: Oh yes I did.

DONNER: You're thinking of that American woman who sang
negro spirituals at Nancy Cunard's coming-out ball.

BEAUCHAMP: It was Queen Mary's wedding, as a matter of fact.

DONNER: You're mad.

BEAUCHAMP: I don't mean wedding, I mean launching.

DONNER: I can understand your confusion but it was Nancy Cunard's coming-out.

BEAUCHAMP: Down at the docks?

DONNER: British boats are not launched to the sound of minstrel favourites.

BEAUCHAMP: I don't mean launching, I mean maiden voyage.

DONNER: I refuse to discuss it. Horrible noise, anyway.

BEAUCHAMP: Only because people have not been taught what to listen for, or how to listen.

DONNER: What are you talking about?

BEAUCHAMP: Really, Donner, you mind keeps wandering about in a senile chaos! My *tape*. If I had one good man placed high up in the BBC my tape would become art for millions, in time.

DONNER: It would not become art. It would become a mildly interesting noise instead of a totally meaningless noise. An artist is someone who is gifted in some way which enables him to do something more or less well which can only be done badly or not at all by someone who is not thus gifted. To speak of an art which requires no gift is a contradiction employed by people like yourself who have an artistic bent but no particular skill.

(*Smack!*)

BEAUCHAMP: Missed!

DONNER: An artistic imagination coupled with skill is talent.

BEAUCHAMP: Where is he?—Ah——

(*Smack!*)

Damn!

DONNER: Skill without imagination is craftsmanship and gives us many useful objects such as wickerwork picnic baskets. Imagination without skill gives us modern art.

BEAUCHAMP: A perfectly reasonable summary.

(*Thump!, fist on desk.*)

DONNER: Beauchamp!

BEAUCHAMP: Did you get him?

DONNER: I am trying to open your eyes to the nakedness of your emperor.

BEAUCHAMP: But Donner, ever since I've known you you've been running around asking for the name of his tailor—symbolism, surrealism, imagism, vorticism, fauvism, cubism—dada, drip-action, hard-edge, pop, found objects and post-object— it's only a matter of days since you spent the entire housekeeping on sugar to make an edible Venus de Milo, and now you've discovered the fashions of your childhood. What *happened* to you?

DONNER: I have returned to traditional values, that is where the true history of art continues to lie, not in your small jokes. I make no apology for the past, but precocity at our age is faintly ludicrous, don't you think?

BEAUCHAMP: At our age, *any*thing we do is faintly ludicrous. Our best hope as artists is to transcend our limitations and become *utterly* ludicrous. Which you are proceeding to do with your portrait of Sophie, for surely you can see that a post-Pop pre-Raphaelite is pure dada brought up to date——

(*Smack!*)

DONNER: Shut up, damn you!—how dare you talk of her?!—how dare you——

(*And weeps——*)

—*and would you stop cleaning the bath with my face flannel!!!*

(*Pause.*) I'm sorry—please accept my apology——

BEAUCHAMP: I'm sorry, Donner . . . I had no idea you felt so strongly about it.

DONNER: (*Sniffle.*) Well, I have to wash my face with it.

BEAUCHAMP: No, no, I mean about your new . . . Donner, what *has* happened?—What happened between you and Martello? You have not been yourself . . . since you smashed your Venus and began your portrait . . . You have . . . shunned me——

DONNER: I did not intend to.

BEAUCHAMP: Have I offended you? Is it about the milk?

DONNER: No. I have just been—sad.

BEAUCHAMP: Do you blame me for Sophie?

DONNER: I don't know. It was a long time ago now. It *is*

becoming a good likeness, isn't it?

BEAUCHAMP: Oh yes. She would have liked it. I mean if she could have seen it. A real Academy picture . . .!

DONNER: Yes.

BEAUCHAMP: I don't know, Donner . . . before the war, in Soho, you were always making plans to smuggle a live ostrich into the Royal Academy; and now look at you. In Zurich in 1915 you told Tarzan he was too conservative.

DONNER: Tarzan?

BEAUCHAMP: I don't mean Tarzan. Who do I mean? Similar name, conservative, 1915 . . .

DONNER: Tsar Nicholas?

BEAUCHAMP: No, no, Zurich.

DONNER: I remember Zurich . . . after our walking tour. God, what a walk! You were crazy Beauchamp, you and your horse.

BEAUCHAMP: I'll never forget it. That really was a walk. When we got to Zurich, my boots were worn to paper. Sat in the Café Rousseau and put my feet up, ordered a lemon squash.

DONNER: The Café Rousseau was Monte Carlo later.

BEAUCHAMP: Monte Carlo was the Café Russe.

DONNER: Was it?

BEAUCHAMP: Put my feet up and ordered a citron pressé in the Café Rousseau.

DONNER: Still doesn't sound right.

BEAUCHAMP: Couldn't have it—no lemons. The waiter was very apologetic. No lemons because of the war, he said. Good God, I said, is Switzerland at war?—things have come to a pretty pass, is it the St. Bernard?—Not a smile. Man at the next table laughed out loud and offered me a glass of squash made from lemon powder, remarking, 'If lemons don't exist, it is necessary to invent them.' It seemed wittier at the time, I don't know why.

DONNER: Voltaire!—of course, the Café Voltaire!

BEAUCHAMP: That was a rum bird.

DONNER: Voltaire?

BEAUCHAMP: No, Lenin.

DONNER: Oh yes. Very rum.

BEAUCHAMP: Very liberal with his lemon powder but a rum bird nevertheless. Edith saw through him right away. She said to him, 'I don't know what you're waiting for but it's not going to happen in Switzerland.' Of course, she was absolutely right.

DONNER: Edith was never in Switzerland. Your memory is playing you up again.

BEAUCHAMP: Oh yes she was.

DONNER: Not that time. That time was Hugo Ball and Hans Arp Max, Kurt, André . . . Picabia . . . Tristan Tzara——

BEAUCHAMP: That was him!

DONNER: What was?

BEAUCHAMP: Conservative. But he had audacity. Wrote his name in the snow, and said, 'There! . . . I think I'll call it The Alps.'

DONNER: That was Marcel. He used to beat Lenin at chess. I think he had talent under all those jokes. He said to me, 'There are two ways of becoming an artist. The first way is to do the things by which is meant art. The second way is to make art mean the things you do.' What a stroke of genius! It made anything possible and everything safe!—safe from criticism, since our art admitted no standards outside itself; safe from comparison, since it had no history; safe from evaluation, since it referred to no system of values beyond the currency it had invented. We were no longer accountable. We were artists by mutual agreement.

BEAUCHAMP: So was everyone from Praxiteles to Rodin. There's nothing divine about classical standards; it's just a bigger club.

DONNER: It seems there is something divine about modern art nonetheless, for it is only sustained by faith. That is why artists have become as complacent as priests. They do not have to demonstrate their truths. Like priests they demand our faith that something is more than it appears to be— bread, wine, a tin of soup, a twisted girder, a mauve square, a meaningless collection of sounds on a loop of tape . . .
(*This is said so bitterly that*——)

BEAUCHAMP: Donner . . . what happened?—what did Martello

say to you?

DONNER: It really doesn't matter. And how do I know he wasn't lying, just getting his own back?—you see, I damaged his figure, slightly . . . He was working on it—I didn't know what it was—And I brought him a cup of tea——

**Flashback**

(MARTELLO *is scraping and chipping, and clicking his tongue, and scraping again. He sighs.*)

DONNER: That's it—help yourself to sugar.

MARTELLO: I'm not getting any. She's set too hard.

DONNER: Knock off one of her nipples.

MARTELLO: I'd need a chisel.

DONNER: Wait a minute. I'll tilt her over. Get the breast into your cup, and I'll stir her around a bit.

MARTELLO: What a ridiculous business. How am I going to sprinkle her on my cornflakes?

DONNER: Starving peasants don't have cornflakes. Good God, Martello, if they had any corn do you think they'd turn it into a sunshine breakfast for figure-conscious typists?

MARTELLO: What the hell are you talking about? What starving peasants? Honestly, Donner, you go from one extreme to the other. On the whole I preferred your ceramic sugar lumps.

DONNER: No, I got the whole thing back to front with my ceramic food. Of course, ceramic bread and steak and strawberries with plaster-of-paris cream defined the problem very neatly, but I was still avoiding the answer. The question remained: how can one justify a work of art to a man with an empty belly? The answer, like all great insights, was simple: make it edible.

MARTELLO: Brilliant.

DONNER: It came to me in my—incidentally, is it you who keeps using my face-cloth to clean the tub?

MARTELLO: No. It must be Beauchamp.

DONNER: That man has absolutely no respect for property.

MARTELLO: I know. And he's taken to hiding the marmalade. Do you happen to know where it is?

DONNER: In the pickle jar.

MARTELLO: Cunning devil! Thank you.

DONNER: The olive oil is really honey.

MARTELLO: Incredible. It probably came to him in his bath, while he was using your flannel.

DONNER: Where is he?

MARTELLO: He went out to get some more sugar, out of his own money. I wonder where he'll hide it.

DONNER: Let him. Sugar art is only the beginning.

MARTELLO: It will give cubism a new lease of life.

DONNER: Think of Le Penseur sculpted in . . .

MARTELLO: Cold rice pudding.

DONNER: Salt. Think of poor villages getting a month's supply of salt in the form of classical sculpture!

MARTELLO: And not just classical!—your own pieces, reproduced indelibly yet edibly——

DONNER: Think of pizza pies raised to the level of Van Gogh sunflowers!—think of a whole new range of pigments, from salt to liquorice!

MARTELLO: Your signed loaves of bread reproduced in sculpted dough, *baked* . . . your ceramic steaks carved from meat! It will give opinion back to the intellectuals and put taste where it belongs. From now on the artist's palate——

DONNER: Are you laughing at me, Martello?

MARTELLO: Certainly not, Donner. Let them eat art.

DONNER: Imagine my next exhibition, thrown open to the hungry . . . You know, Martello, for the first time I feel free of that small sense of shame which every artist lives with. I think, in a way, edible art is what we've all been looking for.

MARTELLO: Who

DONNER: All of us!—Breton!—Ernst!—Marcel—Max—you— me—Remember how Pablo used to shout that the war had made art irrelevant?—well——

MARTELLO: Which Pablo?

DONNER: What do you mean, which Pablo?—*Pablo!*

MARTELLO: What, that one-armed waiter at the Café Suisse?

DONNER: Yes—the Café Russe—the proprietor, lost a leg at Verdun——

MARTELLO: God, he was slow, that Pablo. But it's amazing how
   you remember all the people who gave you credit . . .

DONNER: He gave you credit because you had been at Verdun.

MARTELLO: That's true.

DONNER: It was a lie.

MARTELLO: Wasn't I? It must have been pretty close to Verdun,
   our route was right through that bit of country, remember
   it well.

DONNER: God yes, what a walk. You were crazy, Martello.

MARTELLO: I must have been, I suppose.

DONNER: Beauchamp was crazy too.

MARTELLO: Him and his horse.

DONNER: That was about the last really good time we had . . .

MARTELLO: You hated it.

DONNER: No.

MARTELLO: More than the war.

DONNER: That's what killed it for me. After that, being an artist
   made no sense. I should have stopped then. Art made no
   sense.

MARTELLO: Except for nonsense art. Pablo never understood the
   difference. He used to get so angry about his missing
   arm——

DONNER: (leg . . .)

MARTELLO: I can see him now—a tray in each hand, swearing . . .
   wait a minute——

DONNER: *Leg.*

MARTELLO: A tray in each leg—Are you deliberately trying to
   confuse me?

DONNER: He was right. He understood exactly. There *wasn't* any
   difference. We tried to make a distinction between the art
   that celebrated reason and history and logic and all
   assumptions, and our own dislocated anti-art of lost faith—
   but it was all the same insult to a one-legged soldier and the
   one-legged, one-armed, one-eyed regiment of the maimed.
   And here we are still at it, looking for another twist.
   Finally the only thing I can say in defence of my figure is
   that you can eat it.

MARTELLO: And of mine that you can smile at it. How do you

like her?

DONNER: It looks like a scarecrow trying to be a tailor's dummy. Is it symbolic?

MARTELLO: Metaphorical.

DONNER: Why has she got straw on her head?

MARTELLO: Not straw—ripe corn. It's her hair. It was either ripe corn or spun gold, and I wouldn't know how to do that, it was bad enough getting the pearls for her teeth.

DONNER: They look like false teeth.

MARTELLO: Well of course they're artificial pearls. So are the rubies, of course. I know you'll appreciate her breasts.

DONNER: Oh yes. Are they edible?

MARTELLO: Well, you're not supposed to eat them—I'm only using real fruit for the moment, and real feathers for her swan-like neck. I don't know how to do her eyes: stars seem somehow inappropriate . . . Would you have described them as dark pools, perhaps?

DONNER: Who?

MARTELLO: Well, Sophie of course.

DONNER: Are you telling me that that *thing* is supposed to be Sophie?

MARTELLO: Metaphorically.

DONNER: You cad, Martello!

MARTELLO: I beg your pardon?

DONNER: You unspeakable rotter! Is nothing sacred to you?

MARTELLO: Hold on, Donner, no offence intended.

DONNER: What right have you to sneer at her memory?—I won't allow it, damn you! My God, she had a sad enough life without having her beauty mocked in death by your contemptible artistic presumptions——
(*Thump! A pearl bounces . . .*)

MARTELLO: Now steady on, Donner, you've knocked out one of her teeth.

DONNER (*by now nearly weeping*): Oh Sophie . . . I cannot think of beauty without remembering your innocent grace, your hair like . . .

MARTELLO: Ripe corn——

DONNER: Gold. Your tragic gaze—eyes like——

MARTELLO: Stars——
DONNER: Bottomless pools, and when you laughed——
MARTELLO: Teeth like pearls——
DONNER: It was like a silver bell whose sound parted your pale
     ruby lips——
MARTELLO: *A silver bell!*—yes!—behind her breasts——
DONNER: —were like——
MARTELLO: —ripe pears——
DONNER: Firm young apples——
MARTELLO: Pears—For heaven's sake control yourself, Donner,
     those are real artificial pearls——
     (*Pearls bouncing*—DONNER *thumping, gasping* . . .)
DONNER: Oh Sophie . . . I try to shut out the memory but it
     needs only . . . a ribbon . . . a flower . . . a phrase of music
     . . . a river flowing beneath ancient bridges . . . the scent of
     summertime . . .
     (*Cliché Paris music, accordion* . . .)

**Flashback**

     (*Keep music in. Fade.*)
SOPHIE: I must say I won't be entirely sorry to leave Lambeth—
     the river smells like a dead cat, and the accordionist
     downstairs is driving me insane . . .
     (SOPHIE *is 22 and not at all bitter. Background is sound of
     leather suitcase being snapped shut and strapped up by* YOUNG
     BEAUCHAMP *who is in his mid-20s.*)
     If only someone would give him a job, elsewhere, even for
     a few minutes. Or perhaps we could employ him to take
     down our suitcases. He'd have to put his accordion down for
     that. But then he'd probably whistle through his teeth. I'm
     sorry to be so useless, darling . . . Are the others down-
     stairs? . . . Yes . . . that's them: isn't it awful to know
     voices, instantly and certainly, by their shouts to the
     waggoner five floors down . . . I wish that yours was the
     only voice I knew that well. I like them well enough—
     they are both kind, and your oldest friends, which is enough
     to endear them . . . But I think now—forgive me—but I
     think now—before it is too late . .   I think we ought not to

go with them, I think we ought to remain, just you and I . . .
Darling—please—Please don't do up the strap—say what
you think—it's not too late—Please say quickly, I heard
Banjo's feet across the hall, he'll be up in a moment . . .
(*The strap-noise, surreptitious now, starts again.*)
*Please don't do it up!* . . . not even slowly . . .
(*Wan, affectionate, ironic.*) I can hear the clothes you put on
in the morning . . . Your serge today, hear it and smell it—
with a cornflower out of the vase: I caught that the minute
you put it in your buttonhole—do you sometimes wonder
whether I'm a witch . . .? I'm only your good fairy, if you
let me, and I want to stay here with you. I'll be all right,
after all this time, I'm confident now, I won't be frightened,
ever, even when you leave me here—and of course you will
be going out—often—to visit Mouse and Banjo in their new
studio—Please *say*.

BEAUCHAMP: Sophie . . . How can I say . . .?
(*Door.* YOUNG MARTELLO.)

MARTELLO: Hello . . . So—what news?

BEAUCHAMP: None.
(*Violently pulls strap tight.*)
I'll take this down. How's the waggon?

MARTELLO: All right, but I fear for the horse—bow-backed and
spindle-shanked.

BEAUCHAMP: I'll . . . come back.
(*Door.*)

SOPHIE: I'm sorry not to be helping. I have to sit by the
window and be look-out.

MARTELLO (*laughs openly*): Oh, that's frightfully good. Always
making such good fun of yourself, Sophie . . .
(*Accordion.*)

SOPHIE: Perhaps there will be another accordionist waiting for us
across the river. And no doubt the smell will be much the
same on the left bank. But I shall like the Chelsea side
much better.

MARTELLO: It's a better class of people, of course. Even the
artists are desperately middle-class.

SOPHIE: I was thinking of the sunshine—we'll be facing south on

that bank, and we'll get the sun through our front windows.
I shall sit at my new post, with the sun on my face, and
imagine the view as Turner painted it. It probably has not
changed so very much, apart from the colours. Don't you
wish you could paint like Turner?—no, I'm sorry, of course
you don't, how stupid of me . . . Well, I don't suppose
Turner would have wished to paint like you. He *could* have
done, of course.

MARTELLO: Of course.

SOPHIE: But he would not have wished to.

MARTELLO: It would not have occurred to him to do so; I think
that's really the point.

SOPHIE: Yes, I think it really is. What are you doing now?

MARTELLO: I'm not painting now. I'm making a figure.

SOPHIE: I really meant *now*—at this moment—what are you
doing here?

MARTELLO: Oh. Well, I'm not actually doing anything now, just
talking to you.

SOPHIE: Can you see a hamper anywhere?

MARTELLO: A hamper? —no.

SOPHIE: There ought to be one; for my shoes and handbags.

MARTELLO: Well, wait till Biscuit comes up—I think I can hear
him on the stairs.

SOPHIE: No, that's Mouse. What silly schoolboy names. When
will you stop using them?

MARTELLO: I suppose they are silly when you hear them—but we
never hear them because they are merely our names . . . I
expect we shall stop using them when we are very old and
painting like Landseer.

SOPHIE: Not without lessons. I didn't mean to sound scornful,
about your names. I'm nervous about moving.

MARTELLO: Yes. Of course.

SOPHIE: Nicknames are really very touching. Did you ever play
the banjo?

MARTELLO: No. I was thought to be similarly shaped when
young. Biscuit kept saying, 'Well, that takes the biscuit.'

SOPHIE: Yes, I know. And 'Mouse' because he enters
quietly.

DONNER: Hello, Sophie.
(*Pause.*)
SOPHIE: What *is* going on? (*Pause.*) He told me about your figure.
MARTELLO: Did he?
SOPHIE: Only that you were doing one. What is it?
MARTELLO: Well, actually it's called 'The Cripple'. It's going to be a wooden man with a real leg.
SOPHIE: A sort of joke.
MARTELLO: Yes.
SOPHIE: And will you actually use a real leg?
MARTELLO: Well, no, of course not. I shall have to make it.
SOPHIE: What will you make it of?
MARTELLO: Well, wood . . . of course.
(*Pause.*)
SOPHIE: How about a black-patch-man with a real eye——
MARTELLO: Sophie——
SOPHIE (*breaks—bursts out*): He doesn't know what to do with me, does he?—Well, what's going to happen?—you're all *going*, aren't you?
MARTELLO (*quietly*): Mouse is going to stay. Excuse me . . .
(*Leaves, closes door.*)
(*Pause.*)
SOPHIE (*recovered*): You're staying?
DONNER: Yes.
SOPHIE: Why?
DONNER: Either way it's what I want to do.
SOPHIE: Either way?
DONNER: If you're going with them, I don't want to live so close to you any more.
SOPHIE: If I'm going . . . ?
DONNER: Sophie, you know I love you . . . how long I've loved you . . .
SOPHIE: He wants me to stay? With you?
DONNER (*cries out*): Why do you want to go? (*quietly*) He's stopped caring for you. He only hurts you now, and I can't bear it. When he made you happy I couldn't bear it, and now that he hurts you I . . . just can't bear it——

SOPHIE: Does he love someone else?

DONNER: He hasn't got anyone else.

SOPHIE: That isn't what I asked. Does he love that poet?—that educated Bohemian with the private income?—He read me her poems, and then he stopped reading me her poems. I thought he must be seeing her.

DONNER: Only in company. I'm sure she doesn't think twice about him——

SOPHIE: Is she going with him——?

DONNER: No—of course not! . . . It's not even a suitable place to share like that—it's just one large attic room, the beds all together and just cooking gear in the corner——

SOPHIE: He never intended that I should go.

DONNER: It really is most unsuitable. The bathroom is on the landing below, with steep unprotected stairs—you could fall —Sophie, you *must* stay here, you know it here—and I'll abide by any terms——

SOPHIE: When was he going to tell me?

DONNER: Every day.

SOPHIE: Perhaps he was going to leave a note on the mantelpiece. As a sort of joke.

DONNER: Sophie . . . I love you. I'll look after you.

SOPHIE: Yes, I know you would. But I can't love you back, Mouse. I'm sorry, but I can't. I have lost the capability of falling in love. The last image that I have of love is him larking about in that gallery where you had your first exhibition. 'Frontiers in Art'—what a lark you were, you three, with your paintings of barbed wire fences and signboards saying 'You are now entering Patagonia'—you were such cards, weren't you?, all of you merry, not at all like artists but like three strapping schoolboy cricketers growing your first pale moustaches. I liked you all very much. I like the way you roared with laughter at all your friends. I never heard anything any of you said, and you didn't take any notice of me at the back in my stiff frock and ribbons and my awful thick glasses, but I liked you all anyway, and bit by bit I couldn't stop looking at him, and thinking, which one is he?—Martello? Beauchamp? Donner?

... It was quick: one moment the sick apprehension of something irrevocable which I had not chosen, and then he was the secret in the deep centre of my life. I wouldn't have called it love myself, but it seems to be the word that people use for it.

DONNER: And when you next saw us——

SOPHIE: —I couldn't see you. But at least I no longer had to wear those glasses, and I knew I looked quite pretty ...

DONNER: You were beautiful.

### Flashback

(MARTELLO *and* SOPHIE *are climbing stairs. Above them, behind closed doors, the sound of a ping-pong game in progress.*)

MARTELLO: Quite a climb, I'm afraid ... Five more steps up now, and then turn left and that will be the top floor ...

SOPHIE: It must be a lovely big room ...

MARTELLO: We each have our own room, actually, but we share the drawing room—Left—jolly good show.

SOPHIE: I hear that ping-pong is quite the fad.

MARTELLO: Is it really?—please allow me ...

(*Door. Ping-pong loud. The rally ends with a winning shot— denoted by the hiatus where one has been led to expect, from the rhythm, contact with the 'other' bat.*)

SOPHIE: Good shot!

MARTELLO: Gentlemen, I have the honour to present to you Miss Farthingale.

(*The ping-pong resumes.*)

SOPHIE (*disappointed*): Oh.

MARTELLO: My friends, as you know, are called Mr. Donner and Mr. Beauchamp. Mr. Beauchamp is to your right, Mr. Donner to your left.

(*The ball hits the net: familiar sound of small diminishing bounces on the table.*)

SOPHIE: Bad luck.

MARTELLO: They are not in fact playing ping-pong.

SOPHIE: Oh!

MARTELLO: That is why they are momentarily taken aback. Turn it off, Beauchamp.

(*Cut ping-pong.*)

SOPHIE: I'm sorry.

DONNER (*hurriedly*): How do you do?

BEAUCHAMP: How do you do?

MARTELLO: There's no point in sticking out your hands like that. Miss Farthingale is blind.

BEAUCHAMP: Really, Martello, you exceed the worst possible taste——

SOPHIE: But I am—blind as a bat, I'm afraid.

BEACHAMP: Oh. I'm sorry.

SOPHIE: Please don't mention it.

BEAUCHAMP: I will not, of course.

SOPHIE: Oh, mention it as much as you like. And please don't worry about saying 'you see' all the time. People do, and I don't mind a bit.

MARTELLO: Would you like to sit down, Miss Farthingale . . . Please allow me . . .

SOPHIE: Oh, thank you . . . thank you so much. That is most comfortable. I hope no one will remain standing for me.

MARTELLO: Will you take tea?

SOPHIE: I should love some tea.

DONNER: We were just waiting for the kettle to boil.

MARTELLO: Indian or Singhalese?

SOPHIE: I don't think I'd know the difference.

MARTELLO: Nobody does. That's why we only keep the one.

SOPHIE: And which one is that?

MARTELLO: I haven't the slightest idea.

DONNER: It's best Assam.

(*Kettle whistles.*)

SOPHIE: Is that the gramophone again?

DONNER: Excuse me.

(*Kettle subsides.*)

BEAUCHAMP: I have been making gramophone records of various games and pastimes.

SOPHIE: Is it for the blind?

BEAUCHAMP: Heavens, no. At least . . . the idea is you listen to the sounds with your eyes closed.

SOPHIE: It's very effective. I could have kept the score just by listening.

BEAUCHAMP: Yes!—you see—sorry!—I'm trying to liberate the visual *image* from the limitations of visual *art*. The idea is to create images—pictures—which are purely *mental* . . . I think I'm the first artist to work in this field.

SOPHIE: I should think you are, Mr. Beauchamp.

BEAUCHAMP: The one you heard was my latest—Lloyd George versus Clara Bow.

SOPHIE: Goodness!, however did you persuade them?

BEAUCHAMP: No, you see——

SOPHIE: Oh—of course! Of course I see. What a very good joke, Mr. Beauchamp.

BEAUCHAMP: Yes . . . Thank you. May I play you another?—it's very quiet.

SOPHIE: Please do.

(DONNER *with tea tray*.)

DONNER: There we are. How would you like your tea, Miss Farthingale?

MARTELLO: Perhaps *you* will do us the honour, Miss Farthingale?

DONNER: Banjo!

SOPHIE: Yes . . . Yes . . . I think so.

(*Small sounds of her hands mapping the tea tray*.)

Now.

(*Tea in first. One cup. Two. Three. Four*.)

You will all take milk?

('*Yes please*' *etc. One. Two. Three. Four*.)

Mr. Donner, how many lumps?

DONNER: Two please, Miss Farthingale . . .

(*One. Two*.)

DONNER: Thank you.

SOPHIE: Mr. Beauchamp?

BEAUCHAMP: None for me, thank you.

SOPHIE: Mr. Martello?

MARTELLO: And just one for me.

(*One*.)

SOPHIE: There we are.

(*The men's tension breaks. They applaud and laugh*.)

DONNER: I say, Miss Farthingale, you're an absolutely ripping girl.

SOPHIE: How very kind of you, Mr. Donner. Please do not think me 'fast' but I was no less struck by you and your friends. I thought you all very pleasant-looking and good humoured, and there was nothing I wished more than that I should find myself having tea with you all one day.

MARTELLO: I have not in fact explained to my friends . . .

SOPHIE: Oh, forgive me. I must have puzzled you. My late uncle, who was rather progressive in such things, took me to your opening day at the Russell Gallery last year.
(*Pause.*)

BEAUCHAMP: Forgive my asking . . . but do you often visit the art galleries?

SOPHIE: Not now, of course, Mr. Beauchamp, but I had not yet lost all of my sight in those days. Oh dear, I'm telling everything back to front.

MARTELLO: Miss Farthingale lives at the Blind School in Prince of Wales Drive. She happened to be sitting on a bench in the public garden next to the School when I walked by. She accosted me in a most shameless manner.

SOPHIE: Absolutely untrue!

MARTELLO: I have been twice to tea at the School since then. She always pours.

SOPHIE: I was in the park with my teacher, but she had left me for a few moments while she went down to the water to feed the ducks. When she looked back she saw a gentleman with a fixed grin and a raised hat staring at me in a most perplexed and embarrassed manner. By the time she returned to rescue me, it was too late.

DONNER: Too late?

SOPHIE: I heard this voice say, 'Forgive me, but haven't we met before? My name is Martello.' Of course he'd never seen me before in his life.

MARTELLO: And she replied, 'Not the artist, by any chance?'

SOPHIE: 'I believe so,' he said, flattered I think.

MARTELLO: 'Frontiers in Art?' she asked. I was astonished. And invited to tea; with great firmness and without preamble. Now there you *were* shameless, admit it.

SOPHIE: Well, I lead such an uneventful life . . . I was naturally excited.

MARTELLO: I thought she was going to *faint* with excitement. The chaperone disapproved, even protested, but Miss Farthingale was possessed!

SOPHIE: Please, Mr. Martello . . .

BEAUCHAMP: Well, of course, the chaperone could see what you look like.

DONNER: You must have been very impressed by the exhibition, Miss Farthingale.

MARTELLO: Not by the exhibition at all! (*A bit of a faux pas, perhaps.*) I mean . . . it was Miss Farthingale's opinion that the pictures were all frivolous and not very difficult to do.

BEAUCHAMP: She was absolutely right.

MARTELLO: As I was quick to explain to her. Why should art be something difficult to do? Why shouldn't it be something very easy?

SOPHIE: But surely it is a fact about art—regardless of the artist's subject or his intentions—that it celebrates a world which includes itself—I mean, part of what there is to celebrate is the capability of the artist.

Martello: How very confusing.

SOPHIE: I think every artist willy-nilly is celebrating the impulse to paint in general, the imagination to paint something in particular, and the ability to make the painting in question.

MARTELLO: Goodness!

SOPHIE: The more difficult it is to make the painting, the more there is to wonder at. It is not the only thing, but it is one of the things. And since I do not hope to impress you by tying up my own shoelace, why should you hope to have impressed me by painting a row of black stripes on a white background? Was that one of yours?

MARTELLO: I don't recall it—you asked me about it when we met.

SOPHIE: So I did. Perhaps one of your friends remembers it?— black railings on a field of snow.

MARTELLO: Let me answer for them nonetheless. You seem to forget, or perhaps you do not know, that what may seem very difficult to you may be very easy for the artist. He may paint a perfect apple as easily as you tie your shoelace, and as quickly. Furthermore, anybody could do it—yes, I insist: painting nature, one way or another, is a technique and can be learned, like playing the piano. But how can you teach someone to *think* in a certain way?—to paint an utterly simple shape in order to ambush the mind with something quite unexpected about that shape by hanging it in a frame and forcing you to see it, as it were, for the first time—

DONNER: Banjo . . .

MARTELLO: And what, after all, is the point of excellence in naturalistic art—? How does one account for, and justify, the very notion of emulating nature? The greater the success, the more false the result. It is only when the imagination is dragged away from what the eye sees that a picture becomes interesting.

SOPHIE: I think it is chiefly interesting to the artist, and to those who respond to a sense of the history of art rather than to pictures. I don't think I shall much miss what is to come, from what I know, and I am glad that I saw much of the pre-Raphaelites before my sight went completely. Perhaps you know Ruskin's essay, the one on——

BEAUCHAMP: I say, Miss Farthingale—are you wearing blue stockings?

SOPHIE: I don't know, Mr. Beauchamp. Am I?
      Whatever happened to the game you were going to play me?

BEAUCHAMP: Oh, it's been on. I'll turn the record over for the continuation.

DONNER: You know . . . I think I *do* remember you.

BEAUCHAMP: Now, now, Mouse.

DONNER: A girl—with spectacles, and a long pig-tail I think.

SOPHIE: Yes!

DONNER: I believe we exchanged a look!

SOPHIE: Perhaps we did. Tell me, Mr. Donner—which one were you?

DONNER: Which one?

SOPHIE: Yes. I have a picture in my mind of the three of you but I never found out, and was too shy at the time to ask, which was Donner, and which Beauchamp, and which Martello. I asked my uncle afterwards, but although he knew which of you was which, I was unable to describe you with enough individuality . . .

DONNER: Shame, Miss Farthingale!

SOPHIE: Well, you were all fair, and well built. None of you had a beard or jug ears—and if you remember you were all wearing your army uniforms, all identical . . .

MARTELLO: Yes, it was a sort of joke. We had not been long back from France.

BEAUCHAMP: Late going, late returning.

SOPHIE: A few months later my blindness descended on me, and the result is that I do not know which of your voices goes with the face that has stayed in my mind—that is, all three faces, of course.

(*Pause.*)

BEAUCHAMP: Is it that you remember one of our faces particularly, Miss Farthingale?

SOPHIE: Well, yes, Mr. Beauchamp.

BEAUCHAMP: Oh.

SOPHIE: I mean, I thought you were all engaging.

BEAUCHAMP: But one of us more engaging than the others.

MARTELLO: Ah. Well, we shall never know!

DONNER: Oh!, but it was my eye you caught.

SOPHIE: As a matter of fact, there is a way of . . . satisfying my curiosity. There was a photographer there, for one of the illustrated magazines . . .

DONNER: The *Tatler*.

SOPHIE: No, there was no photograph in the *Tatler*, I happened to see . . . but this man posed each of you against a picture you had painted.

MARTELLO: I see. And you want to know which of us was the one who posed against the painting you have described.

SOPHIE: Well, yes. It would satisfy my curiosity. It was a background of snow, I think.

DONNER: Yes, there was a snow scene. Only one.

SOPHIE: A field of snow, occupying the whole canvas——

MARTELLO: Not the whole canvas——

SOPHIE: No—there was a railing——

BEAUCHAMP: Yes, that's it—a border fence in the snow!

SOPHIE: Yes! (*Pause.*) Well, which of you . . .?

DONNER: It was Beauchamp you had in mind.

SOPHIE: Mr. Beauchamp!

BEAUCHAMP: Yes, Miss Farthingale . . . It seems it was me.
     (*Pause.*)

SOPHIE (*brightly*): Well, is anybody ready for some more tea?

MARTELLO: I will replenish the pot.
     (*Pause.*)
     (GRAMOPHONE: '*Check.*')

SOPHIE: Oh!—is it chess, Mr. Beauchamp?

BEAUCHAMP: It is. Lenin versus Jack Dempsey.

SOPHIE: Oh, that's very good. But do you no longer paint?

BEAUCHAMP: No. Nobody will be painting in fifty years. Except
     Donner, of course.

SOPHIE: Well, I hope you will paint beauty, Mr. Donner, and the
     subtlest beauty is in nature.

BEAUCHAMP: Oh, please don't think that I am against beauty, or
     nature, Miss Farthingale. Indeed, I especially enjoy the
     garden where you met Martello, a most delightful prospect
     across the river, isn't it?—I mean——

SOPHIE: You are quite right, Mr. Beauchamp. It is a delightful
     prospect, for me too. It is only my sight I have lost. I enjoy
     the view just as much as anyone who sits there with eyes
     closed in the sun; more, I think, because I can improve on
     reality, like a painter, but without fear of contradiction.
     Indeed, if I hear hoofbeats, I can put a unicorn in the
     garden and no one can open my eyes against it and say it
     isn't true.

MARTELLO (*returning*): To the Incas, who had never seen a horse,
     unicorns had the same reality as horses, which is a very
     high degree of reality.—Listen! Miss Farthingale, is that a
     hansom or a landau?
     (*Carriage in the street below.*)

SOPHIE: Eight hooves, Mr. Martello, but it's not a landau for all
     that. Those are shire horses, probably a brewer's dray.

MARTELLO (*at window*): A brewer's dray as I live!—More games!

BEAUCHAMP: I say—that has suddenly brought to mind—do you

remember——?

MARTELLO: Yes—I was just thinking the same thing——

BEAUCHAMP: Beauchamp's Tenth Horse!

## Flashback

(*Clip-clop* . . . BEAUCHAMP's *Horse. Flies buzzing in the heat. Feet walking.*)

BEAUCHAMP (*declaiming*): Art consists of constant surprise. Art should never conform. Art should break its promises. Art is nothing to do with expertise: doing something well is no excuse for doing the expected. My God, this is fun. All my life I have wanted to ride through the French countryside in summer, with my two best friends, and make indefensible statements about art. I am most obliged to you, Martello. I am delighted to know you, Donner. How do you like my horse?

MARTELLO: Beautiful, your Majesty.

DONNER: Very nice. Why don't you give it a rest?

BEAUCHAMP: Mouse is a bit mousey today. You should have invested in a horse. It makes an enormous difference. In fact I have never felt so carefree. When we are old and doddery and famous and life is given over to retrospection and retrospectives, this is as far back as I want memory to go——

(*Smack!*)

I've never been so hot . . . and the flies . . .

(*Smack!*)

Are we nearly there?

MARTELLO: Nearly where?

DONNER: How do I know?

BEAUCHAMP: Secondly!—how can the artist justify himself in the community? What is his role? What is his reason?—Donner, why are you trying to be an artist?

DONNER: I heard there were opportunities to meet naked women.

BEAUCHAMP: Donner is feeling cynical.

DONNER: I had never seen a naked woman, and the way things were going I was never likely to. My family owned land.

BEAUCHAMP: Interesting line of thought; don't pretend to follow it myself. I repeat—how can the artist justify himself? The answer is that he cannot, and should stop boring people with his egocentric need to try. The artist is a lucky dog. That is all there is to say about him. In any community of a thousand souls there will be nine hundred doing the work, ninety doing well, nine doing good, and one lucky dog painting or writing about the other nine hundred and ninety-nine. Whoa, boy, whoa . . .

DONNER: Oh, shut up.

BEAUCHAMP: I don't know what to call him.

MARTELLO: I've had the most marvellous idea.

DONNER: So have I.

MARTELLO: A portrait . . . an idealization of female beauty, based on the Song of Solomon.

BEAUCHAMP: I don't get it.

DONNER: *My* idea is that next year we should go on a motoring tour, and if we can't afford a car we should stay at home.

MARTELLO: You were dead keen about a walking tour, Mouse.

DONNER: Well, I like some parts more than others. The part I liked best was the first part when we planned our route, sitting by the fire at home with a cup of cocoa and a map of France. If you remember, we decided to make the journey in easy stages, between one charming village and the next . . . setting off each morning after a simple breakfast on a terrace overhung with vines, striking out cross-country along picturesque footpaths, occasionally fording a laughing brook, resting at midday in the shade, a picnic, perhaps a nap, and then another little walk to a convenient inn . . . a hot bath, a good dinner, a pipe in the tap-room with the honest locals, and so to bed with a candle and a good book, to sleep dreamlessly——

(*Smack!*)

take *that* you little devil!

BEAUCHAMP (*hooves skittering*): Whoa—whoa—Try not to startle my mount, Donner.

DONNER: Oh, shut up, Biscuit. I'm bitten all day by French flies and at night the mosquitoes take over. I nearly drowned trying to cross a laughing torrent, the honest locals have

stolen most of our money so that we have had to sleep rough
for three days, I've had nothing to eat today except for half
a coconut, and as for the picturesque footpaths—oh God,
here they bloody come again!

(*Improbably, a convoy of rattletrap lorries roars past. Between
their approach and their decline, nothing else is audible. At the
end of it,* BEAUCHAMP's *horse is skittering about.*)

BEAUCHAMP: Steady, steady . . . good boy . . .

MARTELLO: Tell you what—give Mouse a go on the horse.

BEAUCHAMP: No. This horse only believes in me. What an
animal!—I've had nine horses at various times counting my
first pony, but none has been remotely like this one . . .
Absolutely no trouble, and he gives me a magical feeling of
confidence. My spirits lift, the road slips by . . . What shall
I call him?

DONNER: Where are we, Banjo? Do you know?

MARTELLO: More or less.

DONNER: Well?

MARTELLO: There's a discrepancy between the map and the last
signpost.

DONNER: There hasn't been a signpost since this morning.
Perhaps they're uprooting them.

(*More lorries.*)

BEAUCHAMP: Steady, steady . . .

DONNER: For God's sake, Beauchamp, will you get rid of that
coconut!

BEAUCHAMP: Coconut!—not a bad name. And yet it lacks a
certain something. Would Napoleon have called his horse
Coconut? . . . Napoleon . . . not a bad name.

DONNER: Apart from anything else, it's becoming increasingly
clear that we should have stayed at home because of the
international situation.

MARTELLO: What international situation?

DONNER: The war.

MARTELLO: What war? You don't believe any of that rot. Why
should there be a war? Those Middle Europeans are always
assassinating each other.

DONNER: That's the fourth lot of troop lorries we've met today, and we haven't seen a newspaper all week.

MARTELLO: The French are an excitable people.

DONNER: But they weren't French, they were German.

MARTELLO: Rubbish.

DONNER: Yes they were.

MARTELLO: Where's that bloody map? Biscuit, were those lorries French or German?

BEAUCHAMP: I don't know, Banjo. One lorry is much like another.

MARTELLO: I mean the soldiers. Donner says they were German.

BEAUCHAMP: How does one tell?

MARTELLO: Well, Donner?

DONNER: The uniforms.

MARTELLO: The uniforms. Well, don't worry. They're going in the opposite direction. By the time they get to Paris we'll be in Switzerland.

DONNER: Do you seriously expect me to walk to Switzerland? You're crazy, Martello.

(*Dull distant explosion; field gun.*)

MARTELLO: Quarrying.

BEAUCHAMP: All right, Napoleon, easy, boy . . .

DONNER: Beauchamp's crazy too.

(*Explosion, repeat.*)

BEAUCHAMP: I know!—I'll call him Beauchamp's Tenth Horse!
—He will be the phantom cavalry that turns the war—now you see him, now you don't—he strikes, and is gone, his neigh lost on the wind, he leaves no hoofprints; there is only the sound of his hooves on the empty road—He's not physical!—He's not metaphysical!—He's pataphysical!— apocalyptic, clipcloptic, Beauchamp's Tenth!—Here it comes—! !

(*A squadron of Cavalry gallops in quickly to occupy the foreground with a thunder of hooves; and recedes, leaving the men stunned and sobered.*)

MARTELLO: Good Christ.

DONNER: Now do you believe me? They were German cavalry.

BEAUCHAMP: He's right.

MARTELLO: We must have got too far east. Don't worry—good God, if a man can't go for a walk on the Continent nowa-

days, what is the world coming to? Come on; I see there's
a fork in the road—judging by the sun the right fork is the
Swiss one.

(*Explosion.*)

Take no notice.

DONNER: Look what's that?

MARTELLO: What?—Ah. Men digging a ditch.

BEAUCHAMP: Soldiers.

MARTELLO: It is not unusual for soldiers to do such work in
France. Or Germany. The main thing is to ignore them.

BEAUCHAMP: That's quite a ditch.

MARTELLO: Isn't it? Laying pipes, I shouldn't wonder.

BEAUCHAMP: Would you call that a trench?

MARTELLO: Take no notice.

DONNER: We'll probably be interned. I hope they'll do it with
some kind of transport.

MARTELLO: Beautiful bit of country, this. The road is climbing.
That's a good sign. Come on, Biscuit. What happened to
your Tenth Horse?

BEAUCHAMP: My feet are swelling visibly—Good lord!

(*A shock.*)

MARTELLO (*talking up and out*): Good morning!

BEAUCHAMP (*ditto*): Bonjour!

DONNER: Gut'n tag . . .

(*Pause*).

BEAUCHAMP (*whisper*): That was a field gun!

MARTELLO: My dear chap, it's nothing to do with us. These
Continentals are always squabbling over their frontiers.

DONNER: How are we going to get back?

BEAUCHAMP: By train. I shall telegraph for money.

DONNER: There won't be any *trains*!

BEAUCHAMP: Then I shall wait at the station until there are.

DONNER: They might think we're spies . . . and kill us. That
would be ridiculous. I don't want to die *ridiculously*.

BEAUCHAMP: All deaths in war are ridiculous.

MARTELLO: Now look here, you two, you're talking like
tenderfeet. I am older than you; I have a little more
experience. I have studied the European situation minutely,

and I can assure you that there will be no war, at least not
this year. You forget I have an Uncle Rupert in the War
Office. I said to my uncle, when they shot that absurd
Archduke Ferdinand of Ruritania, Uncle!, I said, does this
mean war?—must I postpone the walking tour which I and
my friends have been looking forward to since the winter?!
My boy, he said—go!, go with my personal assurance.
There will be no war for the very good reason that His
Majesty's Government is not *ready* to go to war, and it will
be six months at least before we are strong enough to beat
the French.

DONNER: The French?

MARTELLO: Go and walk your socks off, my uncle said, and then
take the waters-waters at Baden-Baden, to which my
auntie added, perhaps that will cure you of all that artistic
nonsense with which you waste your time and an expensive
education. You live in a sane and beautiful world, my
auntie said, and the least you can do, if you must be a
painter, is to paint appropriately sane and beautiful pictures.
Which reminds me—I've stopped being auntie now, by the
way—I was going to tell you about my next work, a
beautiful woman, as described in the Song of Solomon . . .
(*Explosions build.*)
I shall paint her navel as a round goblet which wanteth not
liquor, her belly like a field of wheat set about with lilies,
yea, her two breasts will be like two young roes that are
twins, her neck as a tower of ivory, and her eyes will be like
the fishpools in Hebdon by the gate of Bath-rabbim, her
nose like the tower of Lebanon which looketh towards
Damascus . . . Behold she will be fair! My love will have
her hair as a flock of goats that appear from Mount Gilead,
her teeth like a flock of sheep that are even shorn . . . I shall
paint her lips like a thread of scarlet!, and her temples will
be like a piece of pomegranate within her locks . . .!
(*Explosions.*)

**End of Flashback**

(*The three young men are chanting out directions, sometimes in unison, sometimes just one or two voices.*)

ALL THREE: Left! . . . left . . . right . . . left . . . right . . . right . . . turn . . . right a bit . . . left a bit . . . turn . . . left . . . turn . . . stop!

DONNER: Well?

SOPHIE: I am exactly where I started, standing with my back to my chair.

DONNER: Are you quite sure of that, Miss Farthingale?

SOPHIE (*sits*): There!

(*Gasps; laughs.*)

BEAUCHAMP: You win—but we might have moved the chair.

SOPHIE: I assumed that you would move it back if necessary, or at least catch me in your arms.

BEAUCHAMP: Yes, you may be sure of that.

DONNER: Indeed, yes. In fact, why don't we do it again?

SOPHIE: Not this time, Mr. Donner. I've stayed much longer than I intended, and I don't want them to worry about me at the school.

BEAUCHAMP: Then we'll walk back with you.

SOPHIE: Thank you. But there is really no need to trouble you all.

BEAUCHAMP: I should like to.

SOPHIE: Well, if you would like to, Mr. Beauchamp.

DONNER: We would all like to.

SOPHIE: Goodness, I *will* raise their eyebrows—oh! !

(*She has knocked over the tea-table.*)

BEAUCHAMP: Martello!—you moved the tea things!

SOPHIE: I'm so sorry—how clumsy——

BEAUCHAMP: It wasn't your fault one bit—please get up—really—There!—oh——

SOPHIE: What is it?

BEAUCHAMP: Only that you *are* wearing blue stockings!

(SOPHIE *and* BEAUCHAMP *laugh.*)

MARTELLO: You seem to be in very good hands, Miss Farthingale. I'm sure you don't want to be accompanied by a whole gang of people, so permit me to say good-bye, and I hope that you will come again.

SOPHIE: Oh, Mr. Martello—of course. Thank you so much

again. And good-bye to you both.

DONNER: Oh . . . Good-bye, Miss Farthingale.

MARTELLO: I hope Mr. Beauchamp will not leave you without
inviting you to dinner.

BEAUCHAMP: Wouldn't dream of it.

SOPHIE: I should love to come to dinner. Oh—and there will be
no need to dress . . . Come then, Mr. Beauchamp . . . may I
hold your hand on the stairs?

BEAUCHAMP: If we are going to hold hands, I think I ought to
know your name.

SOPHIE: It's Sophie.

DONNER: Don't fall . . .

BEAUCHAMP: I won't!

(*Their laughter receding down the stairs.*)

DONNER (*close, quiet*): Don't fall.

(*Door closes on the laughter.*)

### End of Flashback

(*Faint accordion as before. Feet descending the stairs, starting
outside the closed door of the room, and getting fainter with
each succeeding floor. They are still faintly audible at the very
bottom, and the last sound, just audible, is the front door
slamming. This whole business probably takes half a minute.
After the slam, SOPHIE speaks close up.*)

SOPHIE: I feel blind again. I feel more blind than I did the first
day, when I came to tea. I shall blunder about, knocking
over the occasional table.

(*Cries out.*) It's not possible!—What is he thinking of?—
What are *you* thinking of, Mouse? . . . We can't live here
like brother and sister. I know you won't make demands of
me, so how can I make demands of you? Am I to weave you
endless tablemats and antimacassars in return for life? . . .
And is the servant girl to be kept on? I cannot pay her and I
cannot allow you to pay her in return for the privilege of
reading to me in the evenings. And yet I will not want to be
alone, I cannot live alone, I am afraid of the dark; not *my*
dark, the real dark, and I need to know that it's morning
when I wake or I will fear the worst and never believe in the

dawn breaking—who will do that for me? . . . And who will
light the fire; and choose my clothes so the colours don't
clash; and find my other shoe; and do up my dress at the
back? You haven't thought about it. And if you have then
you must think that I will be your lover. But I will not. I
cannot. And I cannot live with you knowing that you want
me—Do you see that? . . . Mouse? Are you here? Say
something. Now, don't do that, Mouse, it's not fair—
please, you are here . . . Did you go out? Now please don't
. . . How can I do anything if I can't trust you—I beg you,
if you're here, tell me. What do you want? Are you just
going to watch me?—standing quietly in the room—sitting
on the bed—on the edge of the tub—Watch me move about
the room, grieving, talking to myself, sleeping, washing,
dressing, undressing, crying?—Oh no, there is no way now
—I won't—I won't—I won't—no, I won't . . .!
(*Glass panes and wood smash violently. Silence. In the silence,
hoofbeats in the street, then her body hitting, a horse neighing.*)

**End of Flashback**

MARTELLO: She would have killed you, Donner. I mean if she'd
fallen a yard to the right. Brained you or broken your back,
as you waved us good-bye. I remember I heard the glass go
and looked up, but my mind seized and I shouted 'Look
out' after she hit. I wouldn't have saved you. Beauchamp
said she fell, an accident; otherwise why didn't she open the
window, he said. I don't know, though. Why should she
have behaved rationally to fulfil an irrational impulse? 'This
tragic defenestration,' the coroner said. I remember that.
Pompous fool, I thought. But I suppose he looked on it as a
rare chance to use the word. It's an odd word to exist,
defenestration, isn't it? I mean when you consider the
comparatively few people who have jumped or been thrown
from windows to account for it. By the way, I'm still missing
one of her teeth, can you see it anywhere?—a pearl, it could
have rolled under the cupboard . . . Yes, why isn't there a
word, in that case, for people being pushed downstairs or

stuffed up chimneys . . .? De-escalate is a word, I believe, but they don't use it for that. And, of course, influence. He was bodily in-fluenced. That's a good idea; let's cheer ourselves up by inventing verbs for various kinds of fatality——

DONNER: Martello, will you please stop it.

(*Pause.*)

MARTELLO: Oh, there it is.

DONNER: Her teeth were broken too, smashed, scattered . . .

MARTELLO: *Donner!* If there is anything to be said it's not that. Fifty years ago we knew a nice girl who was due for a sad life, and she jumped out of a window, which was a great shock and certainly tragic, and here we are, having seen much pain and many deaths, none of them happy, and no doubt due for our own one way or another, and then we will have caught up on Sophie's fall, all much of a muchness after a brief delay between the fall of one body and another——

DONNER: No, no, each one is vital and every moment counts— what other reason is there for trying to work well and live well and choose well? I think it was a good life lost—she would have been happy with me.

MARTELLO: Well, Beauchamp thought the same, but they were only happy for a year or two. How can you tell? A blind mistress is a difficult proposition.

DONNER: I would have married her without question.

MARTELLO: Well, yes, perhaps one made the wrong choice.

DONNER: There was no choice. She fell in love with him at first sight. As I did with her, I think. After that, even when life was at its best there was a small part missing and I knew that I was going to die without ever feeling that my life was complete.

MARTELLO: Is it still important, Donner? Would it comfort you if you thought, even now, that Sophie loved you?

DONNER: I can never think that, but I wish I could be sure that she had some similar feeling for me.

MARTELLO: Did you ever wonder whether it was you she loved?

DONNER: No, of course not. It was Beauchamp.

MARTELLO: To *us* it was Beauchamp, but which of us did she see in her mind's eye . . .?

DONNER: But it *was* Beauchamp—she remembered his painting, the snow scene.

MARTELLO: Yes. She asked me whether I had painted it within five minutes of meeting me in the garden that day; she described it briefly, and I had an image of black vertical railings, like park railings, right across the canvas, as though one were looking at a field of snow through the bars of a cage; not like Beauchamp's snow scene at all.

DONNER: But it was the only snow scene.

MARTELLO: Yes, it was, but —I promise you, Donner, it was a long time afterwards when this occurred to me, when she was already living with Beauchamp——

DONNER: What occurred to you, Martello?

MARTELLO: Well, your painting of the white fence——

DONNER: White fence?

MARTELLO: Thick white posts, top to bottom across the whole canvas, an inch or two apart, black in the gaps——

DONNER: Yes, I remember it. Oh God.

MARTELLO: Like looking at the dark through the gaps in a white fence.

DONNER: Oh my God.

MARTELLO: Well, one might be wrong, but her sight was not good even then.

DONNER: Oh my God.

MARTELLO: When one thinks of the brief happiness she enjoyed . . . well, we thought she was enjoying it with Beauchamp but she was really enjoying it with you. As it were.

DONNER: Oh my God.

MARTELLO: Of course, it was impossible to say so, after she got off on the right foot with Beauchamp—I mean, one couldn't——

DONNER: Oh my God!

MARTELLO: Now, steady on, Donner, or I'll be sorry I mentioned it——

DONNER: *Oh my God . . .*

**End of Flashback**

(*Smack!*)

BEAUCHAMP: Missed him again! (*Pause.*) All right, don't tell me
then.

(BEAUCHAMP's TAPE: *snap crackle pop* . . .)

Fascinating, isn't it? Layer upon layer of what passes for
silence, trapped from an empty room—no, trawled—no, like
—no matter: I know that in this loop of tape there is some
truth about how we live, Donner. These unheard sounds
which are our silence stand as a metaphor—a correspondence
between the limits of hearing and the limits of all knowledge:
and whose silence is our hubbub?

DONNER: Are you going out, Beauchamp? I'd like to get on.

BEAUCHAMP: I have nothing to go out for.

DONNER: Get some fly-killer.

BEAUCHAMP: All right, if you'll let me record a clean loop while
I'm out. I don't want you whistling, and throwing things
about when you can't get the likeness right.

DONNER: I *am* getting it right.

BEAUCHAMP: Yes, she's very good. May I make a small
suggestion?

DONNER: No.

BEAUCHAMP: Her nipples were in fact——

DONNER: Get out!

BEAUCHAMP: Courtesy costs nothing. All right, I'll see if
Martello is in the pub, and I'll be back in an hour or so.
(*Changing tapes.*)
There. Will you press the switch when I'm out of the door?

DONNER: Yes.

BEAUCHAMP: Promise?

DONNER: I promise, Beauchamp.

BEAUCHAMP: Poor Sophie. I think you've got her, Donner.
(BEAUCHAMP's *feet down the stairs. Open and close door. The
fly starts to buzz. It comes close to the microphone and the
sound is distorted slightly into a droning rhythm.*)

**End of Flashback**

(*The beginning of the* DONNER TAPE. *It is the same sound as made by the fly.*)

MARTELLO: I don't want to hear it again.

(*Cut* TAPE.)

BEAUCHAMP: Now then. Let's try looking at it backwards. Coolly. Fact number one: Donner is lying at the bottom of the stairs, dead, with what looks to my untrained eye like a broken neck. Inference: he fell down the stairs. Fact number two: the balustrade up here is broken. Inference: Donner fell through it, as a result of, er, staggering and possibly slipping on what is undeniably a slippery floor, as a result of ... Well, fact number three: the sounds which correspond to these inferences were preceded by Donner crying out, preceded by a sort of thump, preceded by two quick footsteps, preceded by Donner remarking, unalarmed—I can't believe it of you, Martello!

(*Pause.*)

MARTELLO: Nor I of you, Beauchamp. (*Pause.*) Well, let's get him upstairs.

BEAUCHAMP: Hang on ...

(*Fly.*)

That fly has been driving me mad. Where is he?

MARTELLO: Somewhere over there ...

BEAUCHAMP: Right.

*The original loop of* TAPE *is hereby reproduced:*

    (*a*) *Fly droning.*

    (*b*) *Careful footsteps approach. A board creaks.*

    (*c*) *The fly settles.*

    (*d*) BEAUCHAMP *halts.*

    (*e*) BEAUCHAMP: ' *Ah! There you are.*'

    (*f*) *Two more quick steps and then: Thump!*

BEAUCHAMP: Got him!

(*Laughs shortly.*)

'As flies to wanton boys are we to the Gods:
they kill us for their sport.'

Now then.

# WHERE ARE THEY NOW?

*A play for radio*

## Note

The play is set almost entirely in two inter-cut locations
School Dinner (1945) and Old Boys' Dinner (1969). Part of
the idea is to move between the two without using any of the
familiar grammar or fading down and fading up; the action is
continuous. For the sake of absolute clarity I have scored
a line across the page at the points where the location changes
but the hope is that these points are in fact self-evident, both
on the page and on the air.

## Characters

### 1945

| | |
|---|---|
| **DOBSON** | late 40s |
| **GROUCHO** | |
| **CHICO** | |
| **HARPO** | } 13 years old |
| **ANDERSON** | |

### 1969

| | |
|---|---|
| **MARKS** | |
| **BRINDLEY** | } Late 30s |
| **GALE** | |
| **CRAWFORD** | 18 years old |
| **JENKINS** | 70 years old |
| **HEADMASTER** | in his 60s |
| | |
| **YOUNG MARKS** | 11 years old |
| **BELLAMY** | 11 years old |

**DOBSON** reappears

In addition, a small group of 13-year-olds is required to chorus one line; and a large number of Old Boys are heard singing the School Song with a piano accompaniment.

*Where Are They Now?*, which was specially commissioned for Schools Radio, was first broadcast on 28th January 1970. The cast was as follows:

| | |
|---|---|
| DOBSON | Carleton Hobbs |
| CHICO | Alaric Cotter |
| ANDERSON | Derek Lamden |
| MARKS | John Bentley |
| BRINDLEY | Brian Haines |
| GALE | David Brierley |
| CRAWFORD | Michael Deacon |
| JENKINS | Godfrey Kenton |
| HEADMASTER | Wilfred Babbage |
| YOUNG MARKS | Judy Bennett |
| BELLAMY | Jean England |
| GROUCHO | Rufus Frampton |
| HARPO | Edward McMurray |

Produced by Dickon Reed

*The* OLD BOYS *are heard taking their places at the tables. The scrapes and murmurs die down to an expectant silence.*

HEADMASTER: For what we are about to receive may the Lord make us truly thankful.

OLD BOYS: Amen.

(*The* OLD BOYS *take their seats.*)

---

GROUCHO: Eurgh!

DOBSON: Pass it along, boy, and be your age.

GROUCHO: I don't like dogfish, sir.

DOBSON: It is not dogfish, it is salmon, *rock* salmon, *finest* rock salmon, caught, quite possibly, off the rocky coasts of our Canadian allies, what is it, Chico?

CHICO: Rock salmon, sir.

DOBSON: Exactly. Why is Harpo weeping?

GROUCHO: He's not weeping, he's praying. It's double French today, isn't it, Harpo?

DOBSON: That will do, boy.

CHICO: Can I have yours, Groucho? You can have some of my strawberry jam at tea.

GROUCHO: I don't want your rotten turnip jam, Brindley, I've got Mexican honey my mother sent from Mexico.

DOBSON: Enough! Who's on tucker today?

CHORUS: Harpo, sir!

DOBSON: Serve the Pom, then, Harpo, and do cheer up. Eat your salmon, boy.

GROUCHO: It's what we had in biology yesterday—fried in batter.

DOBSON: Four C's by tomorrow morning.

GROUCHO: Oh, *sir*!

DOBSON: Even with your parents in Mexico it cannot have escaped your attention for the last five years that there's a war on.

GROUCHO: I think it's off, sir.

DOBSON: You mean the Germans have surrendered?

GROUCHO: The dog salmon, sir.

DOBSON: *Rock* salmon.

GROUCHO: It's off.

DOBSON: Two helpings for you then, Groucho.
GROUCHO: Ugh!
CHICO: He's right, sir.
DOBSON: None for you then, Chico.
CHICO: Oh *sir*!
GROUCHO: That'll teach you, Brindley.
DOBSON: I may look old but I'm not senile. *Root, boy!*
CHICO: Senex—senis—old man!

---

DOBSON: Splendid, Brindley, old man! Splendid to see you! Can I help you to wine—ah, waiter!
(*A gavel bangs. The hubbub is dying down.* BRINDLEY *speaks quietly.*)
BRINDLEY: Oh, thank you, Mr. Dobson.
(*Gavel.* DOBSON *is, apparently, a little deaf now.*)
DOBSON: Does everybody know everybody? What?—Oh!—Ah! Headmaster . . .
(*The* HEADMASTER *is some way off mike, at first.*)
HEADMASTER: Gentlemen, it would not be appropriate to let the whole evening pass before bidding you welcome, and yet I would not wish to belabour you with that welcome while your salmon lies untasted on the plate—so for the moment I will restrict my remarks to expressing my pleasure at seeing so many Old Boys here tonight, and later while you are digesting not only the smoked salmon but also the turkey and the apple pie, I shall have more to tell you of the School and the events of the past year. Until then, as Monsieur Leblanc would wish me to say, bon appetit!
(*He desists amid dutiful chuckles, and the murmur re-establishes itself.*)
MARKS: Leave the bottle, waiter, we'll look after that, there's a good fellow. Pretty unimaginative menu, what, Brindley?
BRINDLEY: Do you think so, Marks?
DOBSON: I don't suppose you know Leblanc, do you?
BRINDLEY: No—Mr. Jenkins taught French in my day.
DOBSON: Leblanc *is* French, of course. I don't really see the point of that. After all I have taught Latin adequately for

fifty years without so much as crossing the Rubicon, eh-eh
. . . ? Still, Leblanc looks better on the prospectus than
Jenkins. The boys call him Chalky, so he must have taught
them *something*.

MARKS: We used to call Jenkins Paddy.

BRINDLEY: Taffy.

MARKS: I mean Taffy. Taffy Jenkins.

DOBSON: Yes, you were an inspired lot.

MARKS: Good of you to say so, sir. I thought we were a cut
above the average. I think most of us have done pretty well
—except Reverend Brindley here, of course—no offence, old
chap—some things are worth more than gold, eh?

BRINDLEY: The correct usage is *Mr.* Brindley. I do wish you
would get these things right. You may refer to me in full, if
you like, as 'the Reverend Jonathan Brindley', or 'The
Reverend Mr. Brindley' but to say Reverend Brindley is as
silly as saying Corpulent Marks. Besides, your assumption
may be premature—after all, the Archbishop of Canterbury
gets seven and a half thousand a year.

MARKS: Did you look that up?

BRINDLEY: Certainly not! It's . . . it's common knowledge, isn't
it?

DOBSON: And what about Mr. Gale here? I've often wondered
what became of you.

BRINDLEY: What! You don't read the right paper! Our friend
Gale is a journalist of considerable repute—a crusading
journalist, I think one might call you, eh Gale?

DOBSON: Oh, I'm very sorry. But your failure to contribute to the
Magazine's 'Where Are They Now?' page does not leave you
entirely blameless, Gale. Nevertheless, it is very good to see
you after so many years. And what do you crusade for?
(*Small pause.*)

BRINDLEY: Mr. Gale has lately returned from Lagos.

DOBSON: Really? How very interesting! What is happening on the
Ivory Coast nowadays?
(*A small embarrassed silence.*)

MARKS (*jovially*): I say, are you going to keep that bottle to
yourself, Gale? It's pretty poor chablis but I'll have another

crack at it. Thanks very much . . . Talking of Jenkins, do you remember his famous Bruiser?

BRINDLEY: My goodness yes, the fearsome Jenkins and his Bruiser—I hope that sort of thing no longer exists, Mr. Dobson?

MARKS: Nonsense, Brindley—never did us any harm—a few thumps with the end of a rope to keep us up to scratch. No good sending a bunch of ninnies into the world, what say you, Gale?

JENKINS: *My* name's Jenkins, as a matter of fact.

DOBSON: Ah, that explains it.

JENKINS: Explains what?

DOBSON: That chair you are sitting in was meant for Jenkins the French, as I understood it—indeed Mr. Gale wrote to ask that he might sit at the same table—but then it transpired that Jenkins the French had in point of fact died——

MARKS: Died?

DOBSON: Quite so. Every master dies in the twelve months preceding one Old Boys' Dinner or another—except for that appalling man Grimes who actually died during one. I shall be no exception. Where was I?

MARKS: Poor chap.

BRINDLEY: Yes indeed. He seemed indestructible. It was part of his fearsomeness.

MARKS: I don't think I was actually *afraid* of him . . .

JENKINS: It does say Jenkins on this place-card.

DOBSON: Exactly. Everything is explained. The chair was not for Jenkins the French, it was for you. What year did you leave, boy?

JENKINS: 1918.

DOBSON: What! You were *below* me! What house?

JENKINS: I wasn't in any particular house as such.

DOBSON: Nonsense! Everyone was in a house. I was in Routledge, as it was then.

JENKINS: Oh. I can't honestly remember now. I was only a weekday boarder, wetlegs they called us, I forget why.

DOBSON: Weekday boarder? No such thing.

JENKINS: There was then. The war, I expect.

DOBSON: I remember the war perfectly well. I was in Routledge.

JENKINS (*helpfully*): I remember I had a colour.

DOBSON: Got your pink? Batting or bowling?

JENKINS: No, no—we were all split up into colours. I was maroon.

DOBSON (*forgetting himself*): You're mad! I may be senile but I'm not completely loco!

JENKINS (*stiffly*): Just as you like. As a matter of fact, I don't remember you either.

DOBSON: Don't remember *me*?! I've been at the School man and boy longer than anyone alive! Did you subscribe to my clock?

JENKINS: Clock?

DOBSON: Obviously not!

JENKINS: I'm afraid I've been out East more or less since I was twenty one . . . Ever been to Malaya, by any chance?

DOBSON (*witheringly*): You mean in the summer holidays? I see they've sewn the slices of lemon into little muslin bags this year. Why do you suppose that is?

MARKS: It's to stop it squirting in your eye.

DOBSON: We've never had muslin bags at the Royal Derby Hotel before. Perhaps there were cases of temporary blindness after last year's dinner.

BRINDLEY: I believe that Mr. Marks was temporarily blind after last year's dinner.

(*The table laughs loudly at this, until* CRAWFORD, *to his embarrassment, is left laughing all by himself.*)

DOBSON: Oh—I don't suppose you know Mr. Crawford, do you?

CRAWFORD: How do you do?

DOBSON: Crawford, on your left, round the table, that's Mr. Gale, Mr. Jenkins, Mr. Brindley, and this is Mr. Marks on my right.

MARKS: You're an *Old* Boy, Mr. Crawford?

CRAWFORD: Yes, sir.

DOBSON: Mr. Crawford left school last term. He was head boy.

MARKS: Good lord!—sorry, Crawford, it's just that in my day the top cap was always a swaggering young blood with a five o'clock shadow and a world-weary manner. How old *are* you?

CRAWFORD: Eighteen, sir.

MARKS: Children! The Upper Henty must be full of children!

CRAWFORD: Yes, sir.

BRINDLEY: Mr. Marks is being heavily ironic, old chap.

CRAWFORD: Sorry, sir.

MARKS: Yes, sir—sorry, sir . . . Do you remember Runcible? And Grant-Menzies? They were kings? Grant-Menzies used a cane with a silver knob and kept a pre-war Lagonda garaged in town. They could reduce the lockers to trembling silence with one look.

DOBSON: Runcible is here—at the Headmaster's table. Do you approve of the new seating arrangements? We've always had the Old Boys' Dinner at long tables in the past, Gale, in the Chatsworth Room downstairs, but we managed to arrange a swap.

MARKS: Speaking for myself I think the change was long overdue. Let the lower decks have the long tables, say I. I like a round table, we've always had a round table at home. I suppose you have a rectory table, Brindley.

BRINDLEY: I think you mean refectory.

MARKS: Long tables always remind me of school. (*jocularly*) Who's on tucker today, eh?

---

CHORUS: Harpo, sir!

DOBSON: So you are—well, jump to it, lad, let's have the pudding in—Oh! Why haven't you been eating? Do you hear me, boy? . . . What did he say?

CHICO: He says he's not feeling well.

DOBSON: Not feeling well? Why should anybody expect to feel *well*? Has he got a mog chit?

GROUCHO: He's just got the frits, haven't you, Harpo?

CHICO: It's all right for you, Groucho—he got as far as you this morning.

DOBSON: All right, all right—do stop crying and take your plate away. You really shouldn't get into such a state over Mr. Jenkins. He no doubt has a thankless task trying to educate

you in a subject that will prove invaluable to you
in later life should you join the Foreign Legion, which
most of you will probably have to . . . No, you can't leave
yours, Anderson; I'm not having any more waste.

ANDERSON: I don't feel well, sir.

DOBSON: If you don't feel well why didn't you go to Staggers
this morning?

ANDERSON: I don't know, sir.

DOBSON: Oh, don't be stupid, boy! I will not tolerate stupid
replies. Very well, go to matron immediately after lunch,
and if she can't find anything wrong with you I'm going to
put you on tunky for the whole weekend—*Have you been
reading at table?!*

ANDERSON: No, sir.

DOBSON: No?—what do you mean, no? Is that a book or isn't it?

ANDERSON: Yes, sir. I wasn't actually reading, sir.

DOBSON: Give it to me at once . . . What's this? Ah! Very well,
since you find this so fascinating, let me have page sixteen
translated into Latin by the morning, as far as 'dit le
boulanger'.

ANDERSON (*dumbfounded*): French into *Latin?*

DOBSON: Now isn't that interesting? It has never occurred to
Anderson that one foreign language can be translated into
another. He assumes that every strange tongue exists only by
virtue of its not being English. Ah—milk pudding!

CHICO: Dried milk.

GROUCHO: Frogspawn.

DOBSON: Put it down then. Thank you.

HARPO: Yes, sir.

DOBSON: Ah! Harpo speaks! You're not mute after all. You just
have nothing to say.

GROUCHO: You can have mine, Brindley.

CHICO: No, thanks, Groucho. It's not milk, it's Klim, I bet you.

DOBSON: Nothing wrong with Klim. Fresh from the Ministry of
Food's prize herd of Jersey wocs. I have just said something
extremely risible—Root, boy!

CHICO: Rido—ridere—risi, I laugh!

(CRAWFORD *laughing solo, slightly inebriated.*)

CRAWFORD: Very good! Very good!

DOBSON (*reprovingly*): It wasn't *that* funny, Crawford.

CRAWFORD (*stops laughing*): Oh, sorry, sir.

DOBSON: Perhaps you had better pass the wine on.

CRAWFORD: Yes, sir, sorry, sir.

MARKS: There you are, Brindley.

BRINDLEY: Oh, I don't think I should have any more . . .

MARKS: Can't say I blame you, old man. I only care for French
wines, myself.

BRINDLEY: It does say Burgundy on the bottle.

MARKS: It's the old wine ramp, vicar! Cheapish, reddish and
Spanish, marks my word or my name's not Mark—or
rather——

(BRINDLEY *giggles.*)

I say, Brindley, you've had enough!

BRINDLEY: Gale has imbibed most of it, with respect——

MARKS: You're welcome to it, Gale, and as for the turkey, I
wouldn't give it to my chow.

DOBSON: Your char?

MARKS: No, my *chow*—an absolute brute, he is, but one needs to
have a guard dog about the place—got a bit of decent silver,
you know . . .

JENKINS (*quietly, under* MARKS): I hope that fellow Marks isn't the
typical Old Boy nowadays, eh Gale? I'll tell you one thing,
he wouldn't have lasted long up country, certainly not in the
old days. The Christmas turkey came out of a tin, if you
were lucky, my goodness yes. Suited me, though. I'll tell
you quite frankly, Gale, after the war I didn't bother with
home leave at all. It wasn't home any more, you see,
not as I knew it. Spent my leaves in K.L. or Singapore.
Mind you, here I am again, and for good. I'll tell you what
it was, Gale. Once I'd retired and life was *all* leave, well I
began to feel I was *abroad* again. Dammit, I was homesick.
(*Chuckles.*) Or schoolsick. I think I came back just to attend
this dinner, for the first time. Like you, I believe. Perhaps
your reasons were similar? I gather you have been working
in foreign climes . . .? The old school *was* my England, you

see; at least it was the part I knew best and thought about, and missed. I had a fine time . . . good friends. We all seemed to belong to each other, you know. Do you know what I mean?

GALE (*quietly*): No.

JENKINS (*unhearing*): I was hoping I might see one or two survivors . . . Bunny Sullivan especially, he was a close friend. And the younger Robertson—his brother was killed in my last year, he was in destroyers. But I don't think I know anybody . . . Mr. Dobson! What happened to Bunny Sullivan, do you know?

DOBSON: You mean *Bunty* Sullivan—and anyway, it wasn't Sullivan. I forget his name but it wasn't Sullivan. I expect you've got mixed up with Seligman.

JENKINS: He was captain of squash.

DOBSON: Fives, you mean.

JENKINS: Was it?

DOBSON: We have never been a squash school. (*Quietly,* to MARKS) You realize, Marks, that that fellow isn't really Jenkins at all?

MARKS (*a quarter drunk*): 'Course not. Jenkins is dead, God rest his soul. (*Piously.*) I'll never forget you, Tommy Jenkins, here's to you, old chap!

DOBSON: No—no—I mean he isn't even the Jenkins he claims to be. There may have *been* a Jenkins, but I don't know this chap.

MARKS: Well, it must be fifty years . . .

DOBSON: I never forget a boy. Besides, he's made several elementary mistakes. I don't know what his game is but he's an impostor.

JENKINS (*to* GALE): He must have been a complete nonentity. If he was there at all. I mean, there's something damned odd about the man—what is he trying to prove with this rigmarole? Dammit, I *played* squash. Personally, I think the old boy is just past it, he's obviously mixing up this school with some other school he was at. His mind's gone. I should know—I had my first cigarette in the squash court! Bunty and I were sick as dogs. Bunny. Oh yes . . . where are they

now, the snows of yesteryear? Life was simpler then. And
England was such a *pretty* place. I swear people were nicer.
I don't remember such desperation over . . . winning the
next trick. Yes, the old school was damned good to me. And
it was all pasture-land then, you know. On long summer
evenings when we were all in bed and almost asleep, we'd
hear the farmer's boy on the hill, calling the cattle home,
singing them home . . . God, yes.

MARKS (*loudly, independently*): Happiest days of my life, to coin a
phrase!

BRINDLEY: Yes, indeed.

MARKS: Love to have them all over again. Still, I've done the
next best thing.

BRINDLEY: What's that?

MARKS: Sent the boy, of course. How's Gerald buckling down,
Crawford? Well-liked lad, is he?

CRAWFORD: Gerald, sir?

MARKS: My boy.

DOBSON (*quietly*): Marks, Crawford.

CRAWFORD: Oh—yes, sir. We don't call him Gerald, sir.

MARKS: 'Course not. Has he got a nickname? Little beggar tells
me nothing.

CRAWFORD: Er, I'm not sure. He's in Junior School, sir.

MARKS: He's got to have a nickname. You haven't been accepted
till you've got a nickname—isn't that right, Chico?

BRINDLEY: Goodness!—I'd quite forgotten!

DOBSON: Oh, yes!—Yes, yes—Gale, Brindley and Marks, we
used to call you the—what was it?—the Three Musketeers,
Chico . . . no, that can't be right . . .

JENKINS (*quietly*): I told you he's past it.

BRINDLEY (*laughing*): No, no—it was the Three Marx Brothers—
Groucho, Chico and . . .

DOBSON: Harpo. Exactly.

MARKS: That was it. Those were the days, eh?

BRINDLEY: Yes, indeed. Did you have a nickname, Crawford?

CRAWFORD: Well, not really, sir.

DOBSON: I regret to say that I am referred to as Dobbin.

MARKS: Dobbin!

DOBSON: Crawford seems embarrassed. Perhaps he thinks I
didn't know? I can't think why—after all, Crawford, you
were aware, were you not, that you were sometimes known
as Crackers?

MARKS: Crackers!

---

CRAWFORD (*viciously*): *Who said that?*
(*Silence.*)
Marks?!

YOUNG MARKS (*scared*): It wasn't me, Crawford.

CRAWFORD (*Caesar*): Come on, I want to know which of you said
that! Bellamy?

BELLAMY: Said what?

CRAWFORD: *My name is Crawford!* Come here.

BELLAMY: We didn't mean anything, Crawford!

CRAWFORD: And you, Marks.

YOUNG MARKS: I didn't do anything, Crawford!

CRAWFORD: You stink, Marks. You stink and you're a wet. I do
not like wet, stinky boys. Do you hear me, Marks? I will not
abide wetness and stinkiness on any account. Why are you
so wet? Don't go away, Bellamy! Now then, Marks,
tell me why are you so wet. How dare you be wet in my
presence? Do you like being wet? Answer me, you moronic
little tick, don't you know that failure to answer a
question offends me, Marks? Take off your shoe, go on
take it off, I'll teach you to be wet——

YOUNG MARKS: You can't, please Crawford, I've got a mog from
matron, I'm excused football, and everything——

CRAWFORD: How dare you answer me back! My God, you're so
wet, Marks, wetness must be beaten out of you—I'm
watching you, Bellamy, don't leave us—bend over, Marks—
(*grabbing him*) *bend over!*

YOUNG MARKS: Please, Crawford! (*Thump.* MARKS *cries out.*)

---

(*Thump. Thump. The* HEADMASTER's *gavel. Silence overtakes
the* OLD BOYS' *Dinner.*)

HEADMASTER: The traditional order of programme will be slightly
different this evening, owing to a very sad circumstance.

DOBSON (*quietly*): I deplore this. Anybody would think that no one had ever died before.

HEADMASTER: I have to inform you that a few days ago, Mr. R. L. Jenkins died in hospital after a short illness. Many of you will remember him with affection and respect.

MARKS: Hear, hear.

HEADMASTER: He was a master for twenty years, and ever since his retirement ten years ago, he has been one of us, a familiar figure at these dinners, and even more behind the scenes, a tireless and selfless worker for the school. It is sad —indeed it is very difficult—to realize that his dapper figure, with gown billowing and moustache bristling, will no more be seen hurrying from Monk's Pond to Chapel, and indeed Chapel will not be the same without his baritone shaming younger men.

DOBSON: Ridiculous fuss.

HEADMASTER: He could be a stern man, but he always had a twinkle in his eye, and I think everyone who was taught by him learned to respect his demanding standards. Like all the best teachers, he had a passion for his subject and the absolute conviction that if it was not necessarily the most important subject, it was the most rewarding. I think it would be fitting, therefore, it before we said Grace, we were to stand for a minute or two in silence and think of Mr. Jenkins, who is now lost to us.

(*After a short pause, the company gets to its feet.*)

JENKINS (*quietly*): I say—Gale! Are you asleep?

GALE (*flatly*): Good-bye, Mr. Jenkins! Or rather, au revoir.

JENKINS: Mr. Gale—we've got to stand for Jenkins.

GALE: I'm sitting down for Jenkins. We stood for Jenkins long enough.

(GALE *is speaking very quietly, but not whispering.*)

DOBSON: Hush!

GALE: And anyway Jenkins has stood me up.

DOBSON: Gale!

GALE: Jenkins, where are you now, now that I really need you?

MARKS: What's the matter with you, man?

GALE: Oh, shut up, Marks. He never taught you anything either.

He made us afraid.

MARKS: Speak for yourself.

GALE: We walked into French like condemned men. We were too afraid to *learn*. All our energy went into ingratiating ourselves and deflecting his sadism on to our friends. We brought him lumps of French to propitiate him until the bell went, and some of it stuck, that's all—right, Brindley?

BRINDLEY: Gale, I beg you—this is not the time.

GALE: Once when I was ill—itself an admission of some obscure failure, you will remember—I spent my time in the San feverishly keeping up with the French I had missed, using my brother's exercise book—he used to lend me it. One day he forgot to pick it up and found himself in a French lesson without any prep to hand in. Jenkins slapped him around for five minutes. (*Gavel.*) . . . What a *stupid* man! I think we would have liked French. It is not, after all, a complex language.

(*The gavel sounds again.*)

HEADMASTER: I can hardly believe my ears. I apologize to those who have had to endure that muttering. I do not know the reason for it but I am profoundly shocked. I will say no more at present. Please be seated, gentlemen, for Announcements, which will be followed as usual by Grace and then the School Song, with our music master, Signor Luzzato, at the pianoforte.

(*The* OLD BOYS *sit down.*)

MARKS: Trust Groucho to make a scene.

---

HEADMASTER (*barks*): Silence!

(*Sounds subsist.*)

First of all I want to draw attention to the deplorable state of the lockers. In future boys who omit to put away their Wellingtons *properly* will be punished. Prefects, please see to it. Next—it has been drawn to my attention that, after last Saturday's away match at Bridlington, certain members of the Second Eleven were seen in the town without their caps and in the company of girls. I must say that I am profoundly shocked by this misuse of trust. The boys have

already been punished, and it is only for the sake of the
school and the team as a whole that I have been prevailed
upon not to bar them from playing in future matches.
However, if there is any repetition of this street-corner
behaviour, I shall without demur have the Bridlington
fixture cancelled.

---

HEADMASTER: But now for some happier news. It is with great
pride and pleasure that I am able to announce to you an
item of news that has brought great honour to the School—
namely that for services to national industry, Geoffrey
Carson has been honoured by her Majesty the Queen with
the Order of the British Empire. Congratulations, Carson
Minor!
(*Laughter and applause from the* OLD BOYS. *The* HEADMASTER'*s
voice and occasional light applause continues under the
following.*)
DOBSON: Why did you come?
GALE: I wanted to see if I'd got him right—if he had any other
existence which might explain him . . . As it is, he'll have to
go to my grave as I remember him. Still, perhaps he
remembered me as a minor bully and a prig, which I
was.
JENKINS: Some of us have happier memories.
GALE: Oh yes, the snows of yesteryear . . . (*Agonized.*) Where
were they *then*? Oh, where the Fat Owl of the Remove,
where the incorruptible Steerforth? Where the Harrow
match and your best friend's beribboned sister? Whither
Mr. Chips. Oh no, it's farewell to the radiators and the
punishable whisper, cheerio to the uncomprehending trudge
through *Macbeth* and sunbeams defined by chalkdust, the
sense of loss in the fruitcake sent from home, the counted
days, the hollow fear of inconsiderable matters, the hand
raised in bluff—*Sir, sir, me sir!*——
MARKS: It wasn't all like that, Groucho. We had good times.
GALE: And Marks has sent his son. God, I wish there was a way
to let small boys know that it doesn't really matter. I wish
I could give them the scorn to ride them out—those

momentous trivialities and tiny desolations. I suppose it's
not very important, but at least we would have been happier
children, and childhood is Last Chance Gulch for happiness.
After that, you know too much. I remember once—I was seven,
my first term at prep school—I remember walking down one
of the corridors, trailing my finger along a raised edge along
the wall, and I was suddenly totally happy, not elated or
particularly pleased, or anything like that—I mean I
experienced happiness as a state of being: everywhere I
looked, in my mind, *nothing was wrong*. You never get that
back when you grow up; it's a condition of maturity that
almost *everything* is wrong, *all the time*, and happiness is a
borrowed word for something else—a passing change of
emphasis.

(*The* HEADMASTER *ceases, the* OLD BOYS *stand up*.)

GALE: Maturity is a high price to pay for growing up.

HEADMASTER: Let us say Grace.

(*There is a general clearing of throats*.)

HEADMASTER: For what we have received may the Lord make us
truly thankful.

OLD BOYS: Amen.

(*General easing movement but all remain standing.* MARKS
*giggles*.)

BRINDLEY: What are you laughing at?

MARKS: Just thinking—for ten years of my life, three times a day,
I thanked the Lord for what I was about to receive and
thanked him again for what I had just received, and then
we lost touch—and I suddenly thought, *where is He
now?*

BRINDLEY (*giggling*): I say, that's not at all funny, Harpo . . . Er,
do you intend to drink your wine?

MARKS: No, no—have it by all means. The brandy's quite
tolerable.

(*A piano chord is sounded. The piano continues to play a couple
of bars of introduction, but* JENKINS *has already accepted the
first chord as his cue to start singing, to the tune of 'Men of
Harlech'*.)

JENKINS:    Sons of Oakleigh, oaken-hearted

Are we ever broken-hearted?
No! . . .
(*The piano falters and dies.* JENKINS' *solo also dies.*)
I say, have they changed the Song?
DOBSON: What school were you *at*, Mr. Jenkins?
JENKINS: Oakleigh, of course. Oakleigh House for the Sons of Merchant Seamen's Widows.
BRINDLEY: Oh dear. I think that's the lot having dinner downstairs, in the Chatsworth Room.
(*The piano has re-started, from scratch. Now—to the tune of* '*Onward Christian Soldiers*'.)
OLD BOYS: Onward fellow Hovians,
Onward into life!
Never mind the struggle,
Never shun the strife!
Spread the flag of Britain
All around the globe!
And the lesson we have learned
In happy days at Hove!

Be the scourge of cruelty
Of heathen be the bane!
It's not so much the runs we score
As how we play the game!
Onward fellow Hovians,
Play it by the rules!
Up for Queen and Country,
Up the dear old school!

Onward fellow Hovians,
Onward into life!
Never mind the struggle,
Never shun the strife!
Spread the flag of Britain
All around the globe!
And the lesson we have learned
In happy days at Hove!

(*During this, for the first time, there is a cross-fade into the past: on an open windy field,* GALE *is playing some sort of game with a few other boys. He is shouting and laughing, calling for the ball, and being called—'Here, Gale! Gale, Gale!'—the voices distant and almost snatched away by the wind. It is a day he has forgotten, but clearly he was very happy.*)

# A SEPARATE PEACE

## CAST

JOHN BROWN
NURSE
DOCTOR
NURSE MAGGIE COATES
MATRON
NURSE JONES

SCENE I: *The office of the Beechwood Nursing Home. Behind the reception counter sits a uniformed nurse. It is 2.30 a.m. A car pulls up outside.* JOHN BROWN *enters. He is a biggish man in his late forties, with a well-lined face: calm, pleasant, implacable. He is wearing a nondescript suit and overcoat, and carrying two zipped grips. Looking around, he notes the neatness, the quiet, the flowers, the nice nurse, and is quietly pleased.*

BROWN: Very nice.

NURSE: Good evening . . .

BROWN: 'Evening. A lovely night. Morning.

NURSE: Yes . . . Mr . . . ?

BROWN: I'm sorry to be so late.

NURSE [*shuffling papers*]: Were you expected earlier?

BROWN: No. I telephoned.

NURSE: Yes?

BROWN: Yes.

NURSE: I mean . . . ?

BROWN: You have a room for Mr Brown.

NURSE [*realisation*]: Oh!—Have you brought him?

BROWN: I brought myself. Knocked up a taxi by the station.

NURSE [*puzzled*]: But surely . . .?

BROWN: I telephoned, from the station.

NURSE: You said it was an emergency.

BROWN: That's right. Do you know what time it is?

NURSE: It's half past two.

BROWN: That's right. An emergency.

NURSE [*aggrieved*]: I woke the house doctor.

BROWN: A kind thought. But it's all right. Do you want me to sign in?

NURSE: What is the nature of your emergency, Mr Brown?

BROWN: I need a place to stay.

NURSE: Are you ill?

BROWN: No.

NURSE: But this is a private hospital . . .

[BROWN *smiles for the first time*]

BROWN: The best kind. What is a hospital without privacy? It's the privacy I'm after—that and the clean linen. . . . [*A thought strikes him*] I've got money.

NURSE: . . . the Beechwood Nursing Home.

BROWN: I require nursing. I need to be nursed for a bit. Yes. Where do I sign?

NURSE: I'm sorry, but admissions have to be arranged in advance except in the case of a genuine emergency—I have no authority—

BROWN: What do you want with authority? A nice girl like you. [*Moves*] Where have you put me?

NURSE [*moves with him*]: And *you* have no authority—

BROWN [*halts*]: That's true. That's one thing I've never had. [*He looks at her flatly*] I've come a long way.

NURSE [*wary*]: Would you wait just one moment?

BROWN [*relaxes*]: Certainly. Have you got a sign-in chit? Must abide by the regulations. Should I pay in advance?

NURSE: No, that's quite all right.

BROWN: I've got it—I've got it all in here—

[*He starts trying to open one of the zipped cases, it jams and he hurts his finger. He recoils sharply and puts his finger in his mouth. The* DOCTOR *arrives, dishevelled from being roused*]

NURSE: Doctor—this is Mr Brown.

DOCTOR: Good evening. What seems to be the trouble?

BROWN: Caught my finger.

DOCTOR: May I see?

[BROWN *holds out his finger: the* DOCTOR *studies it, looks up: guardedly*]

Have you come far?

BROWN: Yes. I've been travelling all day.

[*The* DOCTOR *glances at the* NURSE]

BROWN: Not with my finger. I did that just now. Zip stuck.

DOCTOR: Oh. And what—er—

NURSE: Mr Brown says there's nothing wrong with him.

BROWN: That's right—I—

NURSE: He just wants a bed.

BROWN: A room.

DOCTOR: But this isn't a hotel.

BROWN: Exactly.

DOCTOR: Exactly what?

BROWN: I don't follow you.

DOCTOR: Perhaps I'm confused. You see, I was asleep.

BROWN: It's all right. I understand. Well, if someone would show me to my room, I shan't disturb you any further.

DOCTOR [*with a glance at the* NURSE]: I don't believe we have any rooms free at the moment.

BROWN: Oh yes, this young lady arranged it.

NURSE [*self-defence*]: He telephoned from the station. He said it was an emergency.

BROWN: I missed my connection.

DOCTOR: But you've come to the wrong place.

BROWN: No, this is the place all right. I don't want to be a nuisance.

DOCTOR: Did you try the pubs in the town?

BROWN: I'm not drunk.

DOCTOR: They have rooms.

BROWN: I've got a room. What's the matter?

DOCTOR [*pause*]: Nothing—nothing's the matter. [*He nods at the nurse*] All right.

NURSE: Yes, doctor. [*Murmurs worriedly*] I'll have to make an entry . . .

DOCTOR: Observation.

BROWN [*cheerfully*]: I'm not much to look at.

NURSE: Let me take those for you, Mr Brown. [*The cases*]

BROWN: No, no, don't you. [*Picks up cases*] There's nothing the matter with me. . . .

[BROWN *follows the* NURSE *inside. The* DOCTOR *watches them go, picks up* BROWN's *form, and reads it. Then he picks up the phone and starts to dial*]

SCENE 2: BROWN's *private ward. A pleasant room with a hospital bed and the usual furniture. One wall is almost all window and is curtained.* BROWN *and the* NURSE *enter.* BROWN *puts his cases on the bed. He likes the room.*

BROWN: That's nice. I'll like it here.

NURSE: Will you be all right?

BROWN: Oh yes, I'm all right now. Picture window.

NURSE: The bathroom is across the corridor.

BROWN [*peering through curtains*]: What's the view?

NURSE: Well, it's the drive and the gardens.

BROWN: Gardens. A front room. What could be nicer?

[NURSE *starts to open case*]

NURSE: Are your night things in here?

BROWN: Yes, I'll be very happy here.

[NURSE *opens the case, which is full of money—bank notes*]

NURSE: Oh—I'm sorry—

[BROWN *is not put out at all*]

BROWN: What time is breakfast?

NURSE: Eight o'clock.

BROWN: Lunch?

NURSE: Twelve o'clock.

BROWN: Tea?

NURSE: Three o'clock.

BROWN: Supper?

NURSE: Half past six.

BROWN: Cocoa?

NURSE: Nine.

BROWN: Matron's rounds twice a day?

NURSE: Yes.

BROWN: Temperatures?

NURSE [*turning back his bed*]: Morning and evening.

BROWN: Change of sheets?

NURSE: Monday.

BROWN: Like clockwork. Lovely.

[*The DOCTOR enters with BROWN's form and Elastoplast*]

DOCTOR: Excuse me.

BROWN: I was just saying—everything's A1.

DOCTOR: I remembered your finger.

BROWN: I'd forgotten myself. It's nothing.

DOCTOR: Well, we'll just put this on overnight.

[*He administers Elastoplast*]

BROWN: Must be wonderful to have the healing touch. I should get to bed now—you look tired.

DOCTOR: Thank you. I expect Matron will be along to discuss your case with you tomorrow.

BROWN: My finger?

DOCTOR: ... Well, I expect she'd like to meet you.

BROWN: Be pleased to meet her.

DOCTOR: Yes ... A final point, Mr Brown. This form you filled in ... Where it says permanent address, you've put down Beechwood Nursing Home.

BROWN: Yes. Well, you never know what the future brings, but for the while I like to think of it as home. . . .

SCENE 3: *The hospital office. It is morning, and the* DOCTOR *is at the desk, telephoning.*

DOCTOR: . . . I have absolutely no idea . . . The nurse said it looked like several hundred pounds. . . . His savings, yes. Frankly, I wouldn't be too keen on that—I don't really want the police turning up at the bedside of any patient who doesn't arrive with a life history. . . . I think we'd get more out of him than you would, given a little time, and we'd certainly keep you informed . . . No, he's not being difficult at all. . . . You don't need to worry about that—he doesn't seem very keen to run away. He seems quite happy. . . .

SCENE 4: BROWN'S *private ward.* BROWN *is in striped pyjamas, eating off a tray. A second nurse—*NURSE COATES [MAGGIE]—*is waiting for him to finish so that she can take his tray away.* MAGGIE *is pretty and warm.*

BROWN: The point is not breakfast in bed, but breakfast in bed without guilt. Rich men's wives can bring it off, but if you're not a rich man's wife then you've got to be ill. Lunch in bed is more difficult, even for the rich. It's not any more expensive, but the disapproval is harder to ignore. To stay in bed for tea is almost impossible in decent society, and not to get up at all would probably bring in the authorities. Even if you had the strength of character there's probably a point where it becomes certifiable. But in a hospital it's not only understood—it's expected. That's the beauty of it. I'm not saying it's a great discovery—it's obvious really: but I'd say I'd got something.

MAGGIE: If you'd got something, there wouldn't be all this fuss.

BROWN: Is there a fuss?

[MAGGIE *doesn't answer*]

They should leave well alone. I'm paying my way. . . . Are you pretty full all the time?

MAGGIE: Not at the moment, not very.

BROWN: You'd think a place as nice as this would be very popular.

MAGGIE: Popular?

BROWN: I thought I might have to wait for a place, you know. Of course, it's a bit out the way, no passing trade, so to speak. I'm very fond of the English countryside myself.

MAGGIE: Where do you live?

BROWN: I've never lived. Only stayed.

MAGGIE: You should settle down somewhere.

BROWN: Yes, I've been promising myself this.

MAGGIE: Have you got a family?

BROWN: I expect so.

MAGGIE: Where are they?

BROWN: I lost touch.

MAGGIE: You should find them.

BROWN [*smiles*]: Their name's Brown.

[*The* MATRON *enters: she is not too old, and quite equable*]

MATRON: Good morning.

BROWN: Good morning to you. You must be matron.

MATRON: That's right.

BROWN: I must congratulate you on your hospital, it's a lovely place you run here. Everyone is so nice.

MATRON: Well, thank you, Mr Brown. I'm glad you feel at home.

[MAGGIE *takes* BROWN'*s tray*]

BROWN: I never felt it there. Very good breakfast. Just what the doctor ordered. I hope he got a bit of a lie-in.

[MAGGIE *exits with the tray, closing the door*]

MATRON: Now, what's your problem, Mr Brown?

BROWN: I have no problems.

MATRON: Your complaint.

BROWN: I have no complaints either. Full marks.

MATRON: Most people who come here have something the *matter* with them.

BROWN: That must give you a lot of extra work.

MATRON: But it's what we're here for. You see, you can't really stay unless there's something wrong with you.

BROWN: I can pay.

MATRON: That's not the point.

BROWN: What is the point?

MATRON: This is a hospital. What are you after?

BROWN [*sadly*]: My approach is too straightforward. An ordinary malingerer or a genuine hypochondriac wouldn't have all this trouble. They'd be accepted on their own terms. All I get is a lot of personal questions. [*Hopefully*] Maybe I could *catch* something ... But what difference would it make to you?

MATRON: We have to keep the beds free for people who need them.

BROWN: I need this room.

MATRON: I believe you, Mr Brown—but wouldn't another room like this one do?—somewhere else? You see, we deal with physical matters—of the body—

BROWN: There's nothing wrong with my *mind*. You won't find my name on any list.

MATRON: I know.

BROWN [*teasing*]: How do you know? [*She doesn't answer*] Go for the obvious, it's worth considering. I know what I like: a nice atmosphere—good food—clean rooms—a day and night service—no demands—cheerful staff— Well, it's *worth* thirty guineas a week. I won't be any trouble.

MATRON: Have you thought of going to a nice country hotel?

BROWN: Different kettle of fish altogether. I want to do nothing, and have nothing expected of me. That isn't possible out there. It worries them. They want to know what you're at—staying in your room all the time—they want to know what you're *doing*. But in a hospital it is understood that you're not doing anything, because everybody's in the same boat—it's the normal thing. Being a patient. That's what I'm cut out for, I think—I've got a vocation for it.

MATRON: But there's nothing wrong with you!

BROWN: That's why I'm *here*. If there was something wrong with me I could get into any old hospital—free. As it is, I'm quite happy to pay for *not* having anything wrong with me. If I catch something, perhaps I'll transfer. I don't know, though. I like it here. It depends on how my money lasts. I wouldn't like to go to a city hospital.

MATRON: But what do you want to do here?

BROWN: Nothing.

MATRON: You'll find that very boring.

BROWN: One must expect to be bored, in hospital.

MATRON: Have you been in hospital quite a lot?

BROWN: No. I've been saving up for it. . . . [*He smiles*]

SCENE 5: *The hospital office. The* DOCTOR *is phoning at a desk.*

DOCTOR: No luck? . . . Oh. Well, I don't know. The only plan we've got is to bore him out of here, but he's disturbingly self-sufficient. . . . Mmm, we've had a psychiatrist over . . . Well, he seemed amused . . . Both of them, actually; they were both amused . . . No, I shouldn't do that, he won't tell you anything. And there's one of our nurses— she's getting on very well with him . . . something's bound to come out soon . . .

SCENE 6: BROWN's *ward.* BROWN *is in bed with a thermometer in his mouth.* MAGGIE *is taking his pulse. She removes the thermometer, scans it and shakes it.*

MAGGIE: I'm wasting my time here, you know.

BROWN [*disappointed*]: Normal?

MAGGIE: You'll have to do better than that if you're going to stay.

BROWN: You're breaking my heart, Maggie.

MAGGIE [*almost lovingly*]: Brownie, what are you going to do with yourself?

BROWN: Maggie, Maggie . . . Why do you want me to do something?

MAGGIE: They've all got theories about you, you know.

BROWN: Theories?

MAGGIE: Train-robber.

BROWN: That's a good one.

MAGGIE: A spy from the Ministry.

BROWN: Ho ho.

MAGGIE: Embezzler.

BROWN: Naturally.

MAGGIE: Eccentric millionaire.

BROWN: Wish I was. I'd have my own hospital, just for myself.
I'd have the whole thing—with wards all named after
dignitaries you've never heard of—and nurses, doctors,
specialists, West Indian charladies, trolleys, rubber floors,
sterilised aluminium, flowers, stretchers parked by the lifts,
clean towels and fire regulations. . . . All built round me
and staffed to feed me and check me and tick me off on a
rota system.

MAGGIE: It's generally agreed you're on the run.

BROWN: No, I've stopped.

MAGGIE: Fixations have been mentioned.

BROWN: But you know better.

MAGGIE: I think you're just lazy.

BROWN: I knew you were the clever one.

MAGGIE [*troubled, soft*]: Tell me what's the matter, Brownie?

BROWN: I would if there was.

MAGGIE: What do you want to stay here for then?

BROWN: I like you.

MAGGIE: You didn't know I was here.

BROWN: That's true. I came for the quiet and the routine. I
came for the white calm, meals on trays and quiet efficiency,
time passing and bringing nothing. That seemed enough.

I never got it down to a person. But I like you—I like you very much.

MAGGIE: Well, I like you too, Brownie. But there's more in life than that.

[MATRON *enters*]

MATRON: Good morning.

BROWN: Good morning, matron.

MATRON: And how are we this morning?

BROWN: We're very well. How are you?

MATRON [*slightly taken aback*]: *I'm* all right, thank you. Well, are you enjoying life?

BROWN: Yes thank you, matron.

MATRON: What have you been doing?

BROWN: Nothing.

MATRON: And what do you want to do?

BROWN: Nothing.

MATRON: Now really, Mr Brown, this won't do, you know.

BROWN: Why not?

MATRON: You mustn't lose interest in life.

BROWN: I was never very interested in the first place.

MATRON: Wouldn't you like to get up for a while? Have a walk in the garden? There's no reason why you shouldn't.

BROWN: No, I suppose not. But I didn't come here for that. I must have walked thousands of miles, in my time.

MATRON: It's not healthy to stay in bed all day.

BROWN: Perhaps I'll *get* something.

MATRON: Well, isn't there anything you could do indoors?

BROWN: What do the other patients do?

MATRON: The other patients are here because they are not well.

BROWN: I thought patients did things ... [*vaguely*] Raffia-work ...

MATRON: Does that appeal to you?

BROWN: No.

MATRON: I suppose you wouldn't like to make paper flowers?

BROWN: What on earth for? You've got lots of real ones.

MATRON: *You* haven't got any.

BROWN: Well, no one knows I'm here.

MATRON: Then you must tell somebody.

BROWN: I don't want them to know.

MATRON: Who?

BROWN: Everybody.

MATRON: You'll soon get tired of sitting in bed.

BROWN: Then I'll sit by the window. I'm easily pleased.

MATRON: I can't let you just languish away in here. You must do *something*.

BROWN [*sighs*]: All right. What?

MATRON: We've got basket-weaving . . .?

BROWN: Then I'll be left alone, will I?

SCENE 7: *The hospital office. The* DOCTOR *is on the phone.*

DOCTOR: Well, *I* don't know—how many John Browns *are* there in Somerset House? . . . Good grief! . . . Of course, if it's any consolation it may not be his real name . . . I know it doesn't help . . . That's an idea, yes . . . His fingerprints . . . No, no, I'll get them on a glass or something— Well, he might have been in trouble some time. . . .

SCENE 8: BROWN's *ward.* BROWN *is working on a shapeless piece of basketry.* MATRON *enters.*

MATRON: What is it?

BROWN: Basketwork.

MATRON: But what is it for?

BROWN: Therapy.

MATRON: You're making fun of me.

BROWN: It is functional on one level only. If that. *You'd* like me to make a sort of laundry basket and lower myself in it out of the window. That would be functional on *two* levels. At least. [*Regards the mess sadly*] And I'm not even blind.

Ladies and gentlemen—a failure! Now I suppose you'll start asking me questions again.

[MATRON *silently dispossesses* BROWN *of his basketry*]

MATRON: What about *painting*, Mr Brown?

[*That strikes a chord*]

BROWN: Painting ... I used to do a bit of painting.

MATRON: Splendid. Would you do some for me?

BROWN: Paint in here?

MATRON: Nurse Coates will bring you materials.

BROWN: What colours do you like?

MATRON: I like all colours. Just paint what you fancy. Paint scenes from your own life.

BROWN: Clever! Should I paint my last place of employment?

MATRON: I'm trying to help you.

BROWN: I'm sorry. I know you are. But I don't need help. Everything's fine for me. [*Pause*] Would you like me to paint English countryside?

MATRON: Yes, that would be nice.


SCENE 9: *The hospital office. The* DOCTOR *is on the phone.*

DOCTOR: No ... well, we haven't got anything against him really. He's not doing any *harm*. No, he pays regularly. We can't really refuse. . . . He's got lots left . . .

SCENE 10: BROWN's *ward.* BROWN *is painting English countryside all over one wall. He hasn't got very far but one sees the beginnings of a simple pastoral panorama, competent but amateurish.* MAGGIE *enters, carrying cut flowers in a vase.*

MAGGIE: Hello— [*She notices*]

BROWN: I'll need some more paint.

MAGGIE [*horrified*]: Brownie! I gave you drawing paper!

BROWN: I like space. I like the big sweep—the contours of hills all flowing—I don't paint leaves, I make you see trees in clumps of green.

MAGGIE: Matron will have a fit.

BROWN: What are the flowers?

MAGGIE: You don't deserve them.

BROWN: Who are they from?

MAGGIE: Me.

BROWN: Maggie!

MAGGIE: I didn't buy them.

BROWN: Pinched them?

MAGGIE: Picked them.

BROWN: A lovely thought. Put them over there. I should bring *you* flowers.

MAGGIE: I'm not ill.

BROWN: Nor am I. Do you like it?

MAGGIE: Very pretty.

BROWN: I'm only doing it to please matron really. I could do with a bigger brush. There's more paint, is there? I'll need a lot of blue. It's going to be summer in here.

MAGGIE: It's summer outside. Isn't that good enough for you?

[BROWN *stares out of the window: gardens, flowers, trees, hills*]

BROWN: I couldn't stay out there. You don't get the benefits.

MAGGIE [*leaving*]: I'll have to tell matron, you know.

BROWN: You don't get the looking after. And the privacy. [*He considers*] I'll have to take the curtains down.


SCENE 11: *The hospital office.*

MATRON: It's not as if he was psychotic.

DOCTOR: Or Picasso.

MATRON: What did the psychiatrist think?

DOCTOR: He likes it.

MATRON: About *him*.

DOCTOR: He likes him too.

MATRON [*sour*]: He's likeable.

DOCTOR: He knows what he's doing.

MATRON: Hiding.

DOCTOR: From what? . . . [*Thoughtfully*] I just thought I'd let him stay the night. I wanted to go back to bed and it seemed the easiest thing to do. I thought that in the morning . . . Well, I'm not sure what I thought would happen in the morning.

MATRON: He's not simple—he's giving nothing away. Not even to Nurse Coates.

DOCTOR: Well, keep her at it.

MATRON: She doesn't need much keeping.

SCENE 12: BROWN's *ward.* BROWN *has painted a whole wall and is working on a second one.* MAGGIE *sits on the bed.*

MAGGIE: That was when I started nursing, after that.

BROWN: Funny. I would have thought your childhood was all to do with ponies and big stone-floored kitchens . . .

MAGGIE: Goes to show. What was your childhood like?

BROWN: Young . . . I wish I had more money.

MAGGIE: You've got a lot. You must have had a good job . . . ?

BROWN: Centre-forward for Arsenal.

MAGGIE: You're not fair! You don't give me anything in return.

BROWN: This painting's for you, Maggie . . . If I'd got four times as much money, I'd take four rooms and paint one for each season. But I've only got money for the summer.

MAGGIE: What will you do when it's gone?

BROWN [*seriously*]: I don't know. Perhaps I'll get ill and have to go to hospital. But I'll miss you, Maggie.

MAGGIE: If you had someone to look after you you wouldn't have this trouble.

BROWN: What trouble?

MAGGIE: If you had someone to cook your meals and do your laundry you'd be all right, wouldn't you?

BROWN: It's the things that go with it.

MAGGIE: You should have got married. I bet you had chances.

BROWN: Perhaps.

MAGGIE: It's not too late.

BROWN: You don't think so?

MAGGIE: You're attractive.

BROWN [*pause*]: What are you like when you're not wearing your uniform?

MAGGIE [*saucy*]: Mr Brown!

BROWN [*innocent, angry*]: I didn't mean—!

MAGGIE [*regretful*]: Oh, I'm sorry. . . .

BROWN [*calm*]: I can't think of you not being a nurse. It belongs to another world I'm not part of any more.

MAGGIE: What have you got about hospitals?

BROWN: A hospital is a very dependable place. Anything could be going on outside. Since I've been in here—there could be a war on, and for once it's got nothing to do with me. I don't even know about it. Fire, flood and misery of all kinds, across the world or over the hill, it can all go on, but this is a private ward; I'm paying for it. [*Pause*] There's one thing that's always impressed me about hospitals—they've all got their own generators. In case of power cuts. And water tanks. I mean, a hospital can carry on, set loose from the world. The meals come in on trays, on the dot—the dust never settles before it's wiped—clean laundry at the appointed time—the matron does her round and temperatures are taken; pulses too, taken in pure conditions, not affected by anything outside. You need never know anything, it doesn't touch you.

MAGGIE: That's not true, Brownie.

BROWN: I know it's not.

MAGGIE: Then you shouldn't try and make it true.

BROWN: I know I shouldn't.

[*Pause*]

MAGGIE: Is that all there is to it, then?

BROWN: You've still got theories?

MAGGIE: There's a new one. You're a retired forger.

BROWN: Ha! The money's real enough.

MAGGIE: I know.

BROWN: How do you know?

MAGGIE [*shamefaced*]: They had it checked.

[BROWN *laughs*]

BROWN: They've got to make it difficult. I've got to be a crook or a lunatic.

MAGGIE: Then why don't you tell them where you came from?

BROWN: They want to pass me on. But they don't know who to, or where. I'm happy here.

MAGGIE: Haven't you been happy anywhere else?

BROWN: Yes. I had a good four years of it once.

MAGGIE: In hospital?

BROWN: No, that was abroad.

MAGGIE: Where have you been?

BROWN: All over. I've been among French, Germans, Greeks, Turks, Arabs. . . .

MAGGIE: What were you doing?

BROWN: Different things in different places. [*Smiles*] I was painting in France.

MAGGIE: An artist?

BROWN: Oh very. Green and brown. I could turn a row of tanks into a leafy hedgerow. Not literally. Worse luck.

SCENE 13: *The hospital office. The* DOCTOR *is on the phone.*

DOCTOR: . . . He meant camouflage . . . Well, I realise that, but there are a number of points to narrow the field . . . His age, for one thing. I *know* they were all the same age . . . Must be records of some kind . . . Service in France and Germany, probably Cyprus, Middle East—Aden possibly . . .

SCENE 14: BROWN's *ward.* BROWN *has painted two walls and is working on a third.*

MAGGIE: It's very nice, Brownie. Perhaps you'll be famous and people will come here to see your mural.

BROWN: I wouldn't let them in.

MAGGIE: After you're dead. In a hundred years.

BROWN: Yes, they could come in then.

MAGGIE: What will you do when you've finished the room?

BROWN: Go back to bed and pick up the threads of my old life. It'll be nice in here. Hospital routine in a pastoral setting. That's kind of perfection, really.

MAGGIE: You could have put your bed in the garden.

BROWN: What's the date?

MAGGIE: The 27th.

BROWN: I've lasted well, haven't I?

MAGGIE: How old are you?

BROWN: Twice your age.

MAGGIE: Forty-four?

BROWN: And more. [*Looking close*] What are you thinking?

MAGGIE: Only thinking.

BROWN: Yes?

MAGGIE: Before I was born, you were in the war.

BROWN [*moves*]: Yes. Private Brown.

MAGGIE: Was it awful being in the war?

BROWN: I didn't like the first bit. But in the end it was very nice.

MAGGIE: What happened to you?

BROWN: I got taken prisoner.

MAGGIE: Oh. Well, you're still private, aren't you, Brownie?

BROWN: Better than being dead.

MAGGIE: Being private?

BROWN: A prisoner. . . . Four years.

MAGGIE: Is that where you were happy?

BROWN: Yes. . . . Funny thing, that camp. Up to then it was all terrible. Chaos—all the pins must have fallen off the map. The queue on the beach—dive bombers and bullets. Oh dear, yes. The camp was like breathing out for the first time in months. I couldn't believe it. It was like winning, being captured. Well, it gets different people in different ways. Some couldn't stand it and some went by the book—yes, it's a duty to escape. They were digging like ferrets. They had a hole out of my hut right into the pines. There were twenty in the hut and I watched all nineteen of them go off. They were all back in a week except one who was dead. I didn't care what they called me, I'd won. The war was still going on but I wasn't going to it any more. They gave us food, life was regulated, in a box of earth and wire and sky, and sometimes you'd hear an aeroplane miles up, but it couldn't touch you. On my second day I knew what it reminded me of.

MAGGIE: What?

BROWN: Here. It reminded me of here.

SCENE 15: *The hospital office. Present are the* DOCTOR, MATRON *and* MAGGIE. *The* DOCTOR *is holding a big book—a ledger of admissions, his finger on a line.*

DOCTOR: John Brown. And an address. [*Looks up*] It was obvious. [*To* MAGGIE] Well done.

MAGGIE [*troubled*]: But does it make any difference?

MATRON: What was he doing round here?

DOCTOR: Staying with relatives—or holiday, we can find out.

MATRON: So long ago?

DOCTOR: Compound fracture—car accident. The driver paid for him . . . Well, something to go on at last!

MAGGIE: But he hasn't done anything wrong, has he?

SCENE 16: BROWN's *ward. The painting nearly covers the walls.* BROWN *is finishing it off in one corner.*

BROWN: I was a Regular, you see, and peace didn't match up to the war I'd had. There was too much going on.

MAGGIE: So what did you do then?

BROWN: This and that. Didn't fancy a lot. I thought I'd like to be a lighthouse keeper but it didn't work out. Didn't like the company.

MAGGIE: Company?

BROWN: There were three of us.

MAGGIE: Oh.

BROWN: Then I thought I'd be a sort of monk, but they wouldn't have me because I didn't believe, didn't believe enough for their purposes. I asked them to let me stay without being a proper monk but they weren't having any of that. . . . What I need is a sort of monastery for agnostics.

MAGGIE: Like a hospital for the healthy.

BROWN: That's it.

MAGGIE [*exasperated*]: Brownie!

[*He paints*]

BROWN: Shouldn't you be working, or something?

MAGGIE: I'll go if you like.

BROWN: I like you being here. Just wondered.

MAGGIE: Wondered what?

BROWN: I'm telling you about myself, aren't I? I shouldn't put you in that position—if they find out they'll blame you for not passing it on.

MAGGIE: But you haven't done anything wrong, have you, Brownie?

BROWN: Is that what you're here for?

MAGGIE: No.

[BROWN *finishes off the painting and stands back*]

BROWN: There.

MAGGIE: It's lovely.

BROWN: Yes. Quite good. It'll be nice, to sit here inside my painting. I'll enjoy that.

SCENE 17: *The hospital office. The* DOCTOR *is on the phone.*

DOCTOR: . . . Brown. John Brown—yes, he was here before, a long time ago—we've got him in the records—Mmm— and an address. We'll start checking . . . there must be *somebody.* . . .

SCENE 18: BROWN'S *ward. The walls are covered with paintings.* BROWN *is sitting on the bed. The door opens and a strange nurse—*NURSE JONES—*enters with* BROWN'S *lunch on a tray.*

JONES: Are you ready for lunch—? [*Sees the painting*] My, my, aren't you clever—it's better than anyone would have thought.

BROWN: Where's Maggie?

JONES: Nurse Coates? I don't know.

BROWN: But—she's my nurse.

JONES: Yours? Well, she's everybody's.

BROWN [*worried*]: You don't understand—she's looking after *me,* you see.

[*The* DOCTOR *enters;* NURSE JONES *leaves*]

DOCTOR [*cheerful*]: Well, Mr Brown—good news!

BROWN [*wary*]: Yes?

DOCTOR: You're going to have visitors.

BROWN: Visitors?

DOCTOR: Your sister Mabel and her husband. They were amazed to hear from you.

BROWN: They didn't hear from *me*.

DOCTOR: They're travelling up tomorrow. All your friends had been wondering where you'd got to—

BROWN [*getting more peevish*]: What friends?

DOCTOR: Well, there's an old army friend, isn't there—what's his name—?

BROWN: I don't know. Where's Nurse Coates gone?

DOCTOR: Nowhere. She's round about. I think she's on nights downstairs this week. I understand that you were here once before—as a child.

BROWN: Yes.

DOCTOR: You *are* a dark horse, aren't you? To tell you quite frankly, we did wonder about you—some quite romantic ideas, not entirely creditable either—

BROWN: I told you—I told you there was nothing like that—Why couldn't you—?

DOCTOR: Your brother-in-law said something about a job, thought you might be interested.

BROWN [*angrily*]: You couldn't leave well alone, could you?

DOCTOR [*pause; not phoney any more*]: It's not enough, Mr Brown. You've got to . . . *connect.* . . .

SCENE 19: *The hospital office.* BROWN *appears, dressed, carrying his bags, from the direction of his room. He sees* MAGGIE *and stops. She sees him.*

MAGGIE: Brownie! Where are you going?

BROWN: Back.

MAGGIE: Back where?

[*He does not answer*]

You've got nothing to run for, have you. Nothing to hide. I *know* you haven't.

BROWN: I know you know. They've been busy . . . I wasn't worth the trouble, you know.

MAGGIE: You blame me.

BROWN: No. No, I don't, *really*. You had to tell them, didn't you?

MAGGIE: I'm sorry—I—

BROWN: You thought it was for the best.

MAGGIE: Yes, I did. I still do. It's not good for you, what you're doing.

BROWN: How do you know?—*you* mean it wouldn't be good for *you*. How do you know what's good for me?

MAGGIE: They're coming tomorrow. Family, friends; isn't that good?

BROWN: I could have found them, if I'd wanted. I didn't come here for that. [*Comes up to her*] They won. [*Looks out through front doors*] I feel I should breathe in before going out there.

MAGGIE: I can't let you go, Brownie.

BROWN [*gently mocking*]: Regulations?

MAGGIE: I can't.

BROWN: I'm free to come and go. I'm paying.

MAGGIE: I know—but it *is* a hospital.

BROWN [*smiles briefly*]: I'm not ill. Don't wake the doctor, he doesn't like being woken. [*Moves*] Don't be sorry—I had a good time here with you. Do you think they'll leave my painting?

MAGGIE: Brownie . . .

BROWN: Trouble is, I've always been so *well*. If I'd been *sick* I would have been all right.

[*He goes out into the night*]

# Selected List of Grove Press Drama and Theater Paperbacks

E312   ARDEN, JOHN / Serjeant Musgrave's Dance / $2.45
[See also Modern British Drama, Henry Popkin, ed.
GT614 / $5.95]

E471   BECKETT, SAMUEL / Cascando and Other Short Dramatic
Pieces (Words and Music, Film, Play, Come and Go, Eh Joe,
Endgame) / $1.95

E96   BECKETT, SAMUEL / Endgame / $1.95

E318   BECKETT, SAMUEL / Happy Days / $2.45

E226   BECKETT, SAMUEL / Krapp's Last Tape, plus All That Fall,
Embers, Act Without Words I and II / $2.45

E33   BECKETT, SAMUEL / Waiting For Godot / $1.95 [See also
Seven Plays of the Modern Theater, Harold Clurman, ed.
GT422 / $4.95]

B79   BEHAN, BRENDAN / The Quare Fellow* and The
Hostage**: Two Plays / $2.45 *[See also Seven Plays of the
Modern Theater, Harold Clurman, ed. GT422 / $4.95]
**[See also Modern British Drama, Henry Popkin, ed.
GT614 / $5.95]

B117   BRECHT, BERTOLT / The Good Woman of Setzuan / $1.95

B80   BRECHT, BERTOLT / The Jewish Wife and Other Short Plays
(In Search of Justice, The Informer, The Elephant Calf, The
Measures Taken, The Exception and the Rule, Salzburg
Dance of Death) / $1.65

B90   BRECHT, BERTOLT / The Mother / $1.45

B108   BRECHT, BERTOLT / Mother Courage and Her
Children / $1.50

B333   BRECHT, BERTOLT / The Threepenny Opera / $1.45

B88   BRECHT, BERTOLT / The Visions of Simone
Machard / $1.25

E344   DURRENMATT, FRIEDRICH / The Visit / $2.75

E130   GENET, JEAN / The Balcony / $2.95 [See also Seven Plays
of the Modern Theater, Harold Clurman, ed. GT422 / $4.95]

E208   GENET, JEAN / The Blacks: A Clown Show / $2.95

E577   GENET, JEAN / The Maids and Deathwatch:
Two Plays / $2.95

E374  GENET, JEAN / The Screens / $1.95
E456  IONESCO, EUGENE / Exit the King / $2.95
E101  IONESCO, EUGENE / Four Plays (The Bald Soprano, The Lesson, The Chairs,* Jack, or The Submission) / $1.95 *[See also Eleven Short Plays of the Modern Theater, Samuel Moon, ed. B107 / $2.45]
E646  IONESCO, EUGENE / A Hell of a Mess / $3.95
E506  IONESCO, EUGENE / Hunger and Thirst and Other Plays / $1.95
E189  IONESCO, EUGENE / The Killer and Other Plays (Improvisation, or The Shepherd's Chameleon, Maid to Marry) / $2.45
E613  IONESCO, EUGENE / Killing Game / $1.95
E259  IONESCO, EUGENE / Rhinoceros* and Other Plays (The Leader, The Future is in Eggs, or It Takes All Sorts to Make a World) / $1.95 *[See also Seven Plays of the Modern Theater, Harold Clurman, ed. GT422 / $4.95]
E485  IONESCO, EUGENE / A Stroll in the Air and Frenzy for Two: Two Plays / $2.45
E119  IONESCO, EUGENE / Three Plays (Amédée, The New Tenant, Victims of Duty) / $2.95
E387  IONESCO, EUGENE / Notes and Counter Notes / $3.95
B354  PINTER, HAROLD / Old Times / $1.95
E315  PINTER, HAROLD / The Birthday Party* and The Room: Two Plays / $1.95 *[See also Seven Plays of the Modern Theater, Harold Clurman, ed. GT422 / $4.95]
E299  PINTER, HAROLD / The Caretaker* and The Dumb Waiter: Two Plays / $1.95 *[See also Modern British Drama, Henry Popkin, ed. GT422 / $5.95]
E411  PINTER, HAROLD / The Homecoming / $1.95
E432  PINTER, HAROLD / The Lover, Tea Party, The Basement: Three Plays / $1.95
E480  PINTER, HAROLD / A Night Out, Night School, Revue Sketches: Early Plays / $1.95
E626  STOPPARD, TOM / Jumpers / $1.95
B319  STOPPARD, TOM / Rosencrantz and Guilderstern Are Dead / $1.95

GROVE PRESS, INC., 196 West Houston St., New York, N.Y. 10014